19/4/76

GREEN REVOLUTION

GREEN REVOLUTION

A Case Study of Punjab

M.S. Randhawa

SUKHDEV SINGH	A.S. KAHLON
H.S. MAVI	G.S. KALKAT
S.S. JOHL	M.S. GILL
SOHAN SINGH	HARDYAL SINGH
B.S. PATHAK	G.S. SEKHON
D.N. KALHAN	ASHOK THAPAR

VIKAS PUBLISHING HOUSE PVT LTD
DELHI BOMBAY BANGALORE
KANPUR LONDON

VIKAS PUBLISHING HOUSE PVT LTD

5 DARYAGANJ, ANSARI ROAD, DELHI 110006
SAVOY CHAMBERS, 5 WALLACE STREET, BOMBAY 400001
10 FIRST MAIN ROAD, GANDHI NAGAR, BANGALORE 560009
80 CANNING ROAD, KANPUR 208001
17-19 HIGH STREET, HARLESDEN, LONDON N.W. 10

ISBN   0   7069   0252   1

BOOK DESIGN: ARAVIND TEKI

PRINTED IN INDIA

AT ZODIAC PRESS, NICHOLSON ROAD, KASHMERE GATE, DELHI 110006,
AND PUBLISHED BY MRS SHARDA CHAWLA, VIKAS PUBLISHING HOUSE
PVT LTD, 5 DARYAGANJ, ANSARI ROAD, DELHI 110006

To
The farmers of Punjab
who made the
Green Revolution
a reality
and filled the
bread-basket of India

Glossary

Bajra—Pearl-millet

Berseem—Egyptian clover

Senji—*Melilotus parviflora*

Chari—sorghum

Gowra—cluster-bean

Patwari—village accountant or record-keeper

Bars—Canal Colonies of West Punjab

Jagir—fife

Kharif—summer season or summer crops

Sarpanch—Head of a village *panchayat*

Gramsewak—village guide who advises on agricultural matters, etc.

Moong—*Phaseolus aureus*

Taccavi—kind of loan for agricultural purposes

Rabi—winter season or winter crops

Tindas—a kind of gourd

Bhindis—okra

Bajigars—acrobats

Chaupal—village guest house

Sabha—council

Kisan mela—farmers' fair

Neem—*Melia azadirachta*

Contributors

M. S. RANDHAWA, I.C.S. (Retd.), D.Sc., F.N. I.S.A., Vice-Chancellor, Punjab Agricultural University, Ludhiana

G. S. KALKAT, Ph.D. (Ohio State University), Director of Agriculture, Punjab, Chandigarh

SUKHDEV SINGH, Ph.D. (Louisiana University), Director of Research, Punjab Agricultural University, Ludhiana

M. S. GILL, I.A.S., Registrar, Cooperative Societies, Punjab, Chandigarh

SOHAN SINGH, B.A., LL.B., Managing Director, Marketing Federation, Chandigarh

HARDYAL SINGH, I.A.S., Managing Director, Agro-Industries Corporation, Punjab, Chandigarh

B. S. PATHAK, Dr Agr. (West Germany), Professor and Head, Department of Agricultural Engineering, Punjab Agricultural University, Ludhiana

G. S. SEKHON, Assoc. I.A.R.I., Ph.D. (Iowa), Professor of Soils, College of Agriculture, Punjab Agricultural University, Ludhiana

H. S. MAVI, Ph.D., Assistant Professor of Geography, College of Agriculture, Punjab Agricultural University, Ludhiana

A. S. KAHLON, Ph.D. (Kansas), Dean, College of Basic Sciences & the Humanities, Punjab Agricultural University, Ludhiana

D. N. KALHAN, M.A., Professor Emeritus, Journalism, Punjab Agricultural University, Ludhiana

ASHOK THAPAR, Assistant Editor, *Times of India*, New Delhi

S. S. JOHL, Professor of Agricultural Economics and Sociology, Punjab Agricultural University, Ludhiana

Preface

During the last decade some countries achieved spectacular successes in food production. Thickly populated Japan and Formosa achieved phenomenal increases in rice production. Out of the wheat-growing countries, Mexico is a striking example of a deficit country becoming self-sufficient, and even achieving a small exportable surplus. India, which has been facing a grave food shortage since the Second World War on account of its rising population, has solved its food problem. Although the progress achieved is uneven in different states, it is Punjab which has brought about a real Green Revolution in wheat production.

With the object of analyzing the factors which have promoted the Green Revolution in Punjab, I initiated a study in 1969 in the Punjab Agricultural University. Apart from the Deans of Colleges and Directors of Research and Extension Education of the University, a number of Professors as well as some key officials of the Punjab Government also participated in this study.

The study has revealed that apart from the introduction of high-yielding varieties of wheat from Mexico, there are other factors which are equally important. The human element plays a conspicuous role in agricultural development. A rational policy of land reforms which, however, does not obstruct mechanization is also important. The consolidation of holdings is a *sine qua non* of agricultural development. It leads to rational land use and effective exploitation of ground-water resources with the aid of tube-wells. Rural electrification with a greater use of energy in agriculture is a must.   Rural link roads, linking villages with market towns, are also necessary.   An agricultural university which controls the entire research and education in agriculture and related sciences, and also does a good bit of extension work by providing technical support to extension agencies, is very necessary.   At the same time, each State Government must build up efficient departments of agriculture and animal husbandry.

Similarly, there is need of a cooperative department to provide credit to farmers to promote the use of fertilizers and other inputs. A well-organized marketing federation, whose functions should be to supply inputs and purchase foodgrains from farmers, is most necessary. Again, corporations for agro-industries, dairy and poultry development have been found to be very useful since they can function more efficiently and are less hampered by red-tape as compared to government departments. Finally, the necessity of a price-support policy, so that farmers get remunerative prices for their crops, is the pivot of the Green Revolution.

To understand agricultural development it is necessary to have its historical background. In the preliminary chapters an account is given of the origins of agriculture in the Fertile Crescent in the Middle East in the Neolithic Age.   England is the mother country of the Agricultural Revolution.   To understand the rise of modern agriculture it is necessary to know the development of agriculture in that country in the late 18th and early 19th centuries.

The United States of America contributed the tractor as a versatile tool to world agriculture.   This new tool had a profound impact on agriculture in many countries and is bound to play an effective role in the agriculture of less developed countries.

Chemical fertilizers and plant-protection chemicals, which came into use only very recently in India, and on a sufficient scale after the Second World War in the advanced countries, have played an important role in agricultural production. Hence this study begins with the above-mentioned background information.

It is hoped that this study will be useful to policy-makers and administrators who are concerned with agricultural development in India as well as abroad. It will also be useful to others who are interested in agricultural development, for it has been amply proved that if a country has to make progress even industrially, it must have a sound agricultural base.

M.S. RANDHAWA
Vice-Chancellor
Punjab Agricultural University
Ludhiana

Contents

SECTION I

DEVELOPMENT OF WORLD
AGRICULTURE

1. The Neolithic Agricultural Revolution

Discovery and Cultivation of Cereals and Domestication of Animals. The first Green Revolution began about 7000 B.C. in western Asia in the region embracing Israel, Anatolia, Mesopotamia, the Caspian Basin and the adjoining Iranian plateau, called the Fertile Crescent. This region is the birthplace of agriculture, and in it are found the wild ancestors of two major cereals, wheat and barley, and of domesticated animals like cattle, sheep, goat and pig. It was here that man made selections from the seeds of wild wheat and barley and sowed them. It was here that the domestication of cattle, pigs, goats, sheep and later on of horses took place. From this region Neolithic culture spread in a series of waves to the Aegean, the Levant and Egypt (sixth millennium), south Russia, the Balkans and the Danube Valley (early fifth millennium), and Italy, France and Spain (late fifth millennium). In the third millennium it reached northern India, the regions of Sind, Punjab, Rajasthan, and Gujarat. It reached the British Isles as late as 2000 B.C.

In the mountainous area extending from the Caucasus to Afghanistan also originated most of the important legumes, Asian cottons, small-seeded flax, many oilseed plants, onions, and almost all the fruits, such as plums, apricots, peaches, almonds, cherries, apples, pears, grapes, walnuts, strawberries, gooseberries and blackberries, cultivated in the temperate parts of the world. Abyssinia is the home of hard wheats, barley, millets, sorghums, sesame and coffee.

The original plough of the Mesopotamians was merely a curved stick to which a flint hoe was tied to act as a ploughshare.

Apart from the discovery of agriculture and animal husbandry, the other achievements of the Neolithic revolution were polished-stone implements, woodworking, construction of houses and making of pottery and textiles.

The territory extending from the mountains of north-eastern India to southern and central China is the homeland of tea, soyabean, litchi and citrus fruits. In this region China was the centre of the Neolithic agricultural revolution with rice as the cereal crop and tea as its beverage.

In the New World the centre of the agricultural revolution was the area of Mexico, Peru and Bolivia. In the third millennium B.C. potato, sweet-potato, cassava, bean, tomato, pumpkin, chilli, papaya, pineapple, guava, custard-apple, sapota, cacao, groundnut and cashewnut were cultivated in this region of the New World. Maize, their staple food crop, was cultivated in the second millennium B.C.

The Indo-Malayan area is the home of banana, coconut, sugarcane, mango and many other tropical fruits. Rice also probably originated in this area or perhaps in the Philippines.

By about 2500 B.C. Punjab, Sind and parts of Rajasthan and Gujarat had settled villages and wheat and barley were cultivated. Along with the polished-stone implements, brass and copper implements also came into use. That is why it is called Chalcolithic or Copper-Stone Age. The system of nomadic, shifting cultivation gave way to the cereal-fallow system. Irrigated farming was practised, canals were dug and floodwaters were stored in reservoirs. Along with flint hoes, copper and bronze axes were also in use. By that time the wheel had been invented. Metal-working in copper, bronze and gold, and the making of glass and basketry had been achieved. The people of this old culture cultivated land irrigated by annual floods of rivers. They grew wheat, barley and cotton of coarse types and had short-horned zebu cattle, water buffaloes, camels, sheep, pigs and fowls. Bullock-carts with solid wheels were used for transport. The cultivation of rice came about 2000 B.C. in Orissa and Bengal.

The new techniques of food growing also led to a population explosion in the areas which came under the sweep of the Neolithic Green Revolution. According to Kosambi, the most efficient hunting and food gathering can hardly support one person per square kilometre, pastoral life can support three, and agriculture about a 100. The population of England and Wales was estimated by Graham Clark at 250 human beings in the Palaeolithic period, 4,500 in the Mesolithic, 20,000 in the Neolithic and about 40,000 in the second millennium B.C. So we can surmise that by the close of the Neolithic period, the countries mentioned earlier were rapidly filled up with people.

The Second Agricultural Revolution. Mastery of Iron Technology. The Aryans came to India from a region near the Caspian about 1600 B.C. They were Bronze Age people. In the battlefield with their bronze swords and horse-drawn chariots they established their superiority over the town dwellers of Mohenjo-Daro, Harappa, Ropar, etc. Their main cereal was barley. They had horses, cattle, sheep and goats. The horse was their sacred animal which they ceremonially sacrificed.

The second agricultural revolution took place after the discovery of iron about 1000 B.C. Soon iron technology was mastered and with the aid of the iron-tipped plough large areas were brought under cultivation all over the world. In India it led to the conquest of the jungle-infested areas of Uttar Pradesh and Bihar, which became the centre of the Aryan civilization. Jungles were cleared and large areas came under cultivation. From standards current in those times India was a prosperous country and remained so up to A.D. 1000. In agriculture, however, apart from the use of organic manure and the bullock-drawn plough there was no remarkable change. This was largely due to the caste system which perpetuated schisms between brain-workers and manual workers. Agriculture became the preserve of the least intelligent, and remained so for many centuries which followed. That is why, unlike ancient Rome, India did not produce a Cato or a Pliny.

The Third Agricultural Revolution. The Discovery of Legume-rotation System. Agriculture was highly prized by the Romans for there was independence in the farmer's life and health in his work. The Roman senator derived his moral strength and character from his rural background.

The countries bordering upon the Mediterranean on the north are the native home of oats, beets, figs, large-seeded flax, cabbages, cauliflowers and other cultivated forms of *Brassica oleracea* and some legumes.

The credit for the third agricultural revolution can be given to the Romans who developed the legume-rotation system. Before this the naked-fallow system prevailed; the land was left fallow, and was used as a sheep pasture, and in due course the weeds and the sheep manure were ploughed in. The Romans adopted the cultivation of leguminous crops like beans, peas, lupine and lucerne which enrich the soil with nitrogen. These leguminous crops were rotated with wheat, rye, barley and oats.

The earliest of the Roman chroniclers of agricultural practices was Cato (243-147 B.C.). He regarded farmers as the best citizens and soldiers. According to him, the farmers' business was to sell the maximum and buy the minimum. Olive oil, wine, cattle, sheep and worthless slaves who were sick and old were to be disposed of at the best price obtainable. Varro (about 50 B.C.), statesman, scholar and gentleman farmer, wrote a number of treatises on the cultivation of wheat, legumes, grapevines and olive trees as well as on the raising of cattle, sheep, goats, pigs, asses and horses. Varro was followed by Columella and Pliny in the first century of the Christian Era. These writers on agriculture left a valuable record of agricultural practices of the age, and inspired many successors.

2. Agricultural Revolution in England

The commercial revolution in England began in the sixteenth century with the growth of overseas trade. Trading companies were formed and commerce was concentrated in large cities, particularly in London. In the seventeenth century, the agricultural revolution began in England and contemporaneous with it was the industrial revolution. It saw the disappearance of the naked-fallow system and the decline of field-grass husbandry. Its main achievements were the scientific rotation of crops and the adoption of new implements from the Continent. Before this only hand-tools like the flail, the hand-hoe, the sickle, the scythe, the spade, and the fork were in use. As Gras observes, "The agricultural revolution was made in England out of Continental materials: Spanish clover, Burgundian and French grasses, the Dutch plough, the horse-hoe of Languedoc, and the Flemish method of cultivating turnips in fields. No earlier change in agricultural technique displayed such a rare combination of speed of development, extent of improvement, and degree of acceptance."[1]

From 1770 onwards new agriculture rapidly spread in England. A balance was struck between tillage and cattle-breeding. Intensive agriculture with truck-gardening and fruit-farming on smaller holdings was established. Improvements in agriculture were made not by professional farmers but by men with cultivated minds who adopted it as a recreation or with the

[1]Norman Scott Brien Gras, *A History of Agriculture in Europe and America*, London, pp. 208, 209.

desire of improving what they saw being imperfectly performed. Jethro Tull (1674-1741), the Morning Star of the agricultural revolution, was a gentleman farmer, educated at Oxford. He began to apply his intelligence and sense of observation to the problems of agriculture to make it more efficient. By inventing the seed-drill he did away with the broadcasting of seed. He also invented the horse-hoe. Andrew Meikle, a Scotsman, invented the threshing-machine in 1784.

The rise in the price of agricultural products, particularly wheat which cost three times more during the French Revolution and the Napoleonic War (1793-1815), gave a great stimulus to agriculture, and the use of new implements and machinery accelerated further progress.

The eighteenth century also saw the rise of agriculture as a profession. A professorship in agriculture was established at Edinburgh in 1790. Societies for the improvement of cultivation were formed in Scotland in 1723 and in the west of England in 1777. The *Farmers Magazine*, a monthly, was established in 1776.

The pioneers of the agricultural revolution were not farmers by profession but amateurs who had amassed wealth in trade and invested it in farming. The rise in the price of agricultural products provided the most powerful stimulus. The agricultural and industrial revolutions had a great impact on land development. As G.M. Trevelyan observes:

The capital created by the incipient industrial revolution was much of it conducted by the channel of the great-estate system to fertilize agriculture with money derived from cloth, cotton, coal, and commerce. But capital also flowed in the opposite direction, from land into industry: many of the new industrialists who set up factories, mills, and businesses in the eighteenth century, derived the money they so employed from their own or their fathers' success as cultivators of the land. The country banks, now growing up in great numbers, assisted this double flow of capital from industry into agriculture and from agriculture into industry.[2]

[2] G.M. Trevelyan, *Illustrated English Social History*, p. 136.

The agricultural revolution dealt a heavy blow to the peasant proprietors, the yeomen and customary tenants. Great compact estates were created. The peasant proprietors, cottars and squatters disappeared. This was a great social loss. However, the enclosures led to fencing of fields by live hedges and facilitated the adoption of new methods of draining land.

The agricultural revolution proved a great boon to cattle. On account of shortage of food in winter all except the breeding stock used to be slaughtered and the survivors were kept on short rations until spring when grass grew. On account of the enclosures more arable land was used for raising grass and turnips to feed the cattle and sheep through the winter. With better feeding and selection the average weight of cattle and sheep doubled between 1710 and 1795.

"The English by their industrial and agricultural revolutions blazed a trail for the whole world," observes Trevelyan. However, the social price they paid was also heavy. The yeomen, the peasant proprietors, who were the flower of the British Army, practically disappeared. Many of them migrated to America or joined industry as workers. France, on the other hand, retained her farmers, and managed to stabilize her population through birth control.

British agriculture reached its peak of prosperity about 1870. In the seventies it collapsed on account of competition with the American farmers who, on account of their abundant natural resources and rich soil, could produce wheat cheaper than the British.

3. The American Agricultural Revolution

The Coming of the Tractor. The American continents, North and South, received the overflow of surplus European population. The English, the Irish, the Dutch and the French settled in North America, and the Spanish and the Portuguese in Central and South America. The first British colony in North America, New England, was settled in 1620. Gradually the population increased by reproduction and the arrival of new immigrants.

In 1840-50, the railways were built and the central plains, the rich prairies, were colonized. These areas enjoyed grassland climate, and were ideal for wheat and maize production under rain-fed conditions. Increase in the production of foodgrains during this period was owing to expansion in acreage rather than to any innovation.

Here it would be pertinent to refer to an important development in education. Colleges and universities in the U.S.A. were devoted to arts, the humanities and basic sciences. In 1862 the Land Grant Colleges were established by the Federal Government under the Morrill Act with the specific requirement that they would provide a sound practical education in agriculture and engineering. They were designed to serve agriculture. These colleges are generally agreed to have been the most important single factor in the development of American agriculture.

The Land Grant Institutions made intensive tests of varieties of all crops, and recommended those that proved best. They worked out crop-rotation systems for different types of farming. They planned breeding and feeding practices for cattle, hogs, sheep, horses, and poultry. The engineers worked out schemes for drainage and irrigation, and developed plans for farm buildings. In short, every facet of farm business was explored in a very practical way. Improved varieties of crops and breeds of animals were developed. Essentially, all the foundations necessary for a great agricultural expansion were laid.

In 1890, an important development took place in the wheat farms of north-western United States. This was in the form of tractors which were large four-wheeled machines driven by steam and could pull as many as 40 ploughs across the field. The first gasoline tractor was built in 1892 by John Froelich, an Iowa farmer and blacksmith. In 1910, the combined mechanical and animal power on U.S. farms totalled 28,000,000 h.p. of which mechanical power, largely steam, represented 6,500,000 h.p. or about 24 per cent of the total. By 1912, steam tractors attained their peak of size and performance. After a lapse of 12 years they became extinct.

In 1910, tractors with internal-combustion engines were developed. In 1918, the United States, in its second year of entry in the World War, was confronted with a severe shortage of farm labour. Mass production of tractors with internal-combustion engines was started. The most significant design development was the introduction of the rear-power take-off for the operation of mounted and drawn implements. Originally regarded as an alternative to the horse, the tractor has now come to be regarded more as a versatile source of power with a part to play in most farming operations, e.g. ploughing, harrowing, planting, cultivating, harvesting and threshing. In 1931, tractors were equipped with diesel engines which enabled these machines to work under extremely adverse traction conditions. Low-pressure pneumatic tyres first appeared on the farm tractors about 1932.

Tractors began to replace horses and mules rapidly. Less labour had to be hired, and less land was needed to produce feed for the draft animals. In fact, the acreage needed to support the horses and mules of the country dropped from the maximum of 70 million acres to around 50 million acres in the late 1930s and is presently less than four million acres—largely to support horses for recreational purposes. Work animals on farms are almost non-existent today. Large tractors reached a total of about 1.5 million by 1940 and increased phenomenally thereafter.

World War II provided price incentives for another great surge in agricultural production. Labour became not only very expensive, but unobtainable. To increase the output per man on the farm, there was a very strong move towards mechanization. By the end of the War there were 2.5 million large tractors on farms.

Large tractors pull machinery for cultivation followed by a grain-drill, thus preparing the land and planting the crop in one operation, and require only minutes for one operator for each acre. Harvesting and threshing with the largest combines available can be done at the rate of ten acres per hour, or six minutes per acre. The total human labour inputs for land preparation, seeding, harvesting and threshing one acre of wheat can be less than one hour.

By 1960 the world tractor population had reached about ten million and over half of these were in North America. In 1959 the number of arable acres to each agricultural tractor was about 16 in New Zealand, 27 in West Germany, 40 to 45 in the U.K., Norway and the Netherlands, 100 in Canada and the U.S.A., over 250 in South Africa and Australia, 820 in Argentina, 15,000 in Pakistan and 19,000 in India. The distribution of tractors in the main countries of the world is given below:

Table 1

Name of the country	Riding tractors (1,000)	Walking tractors (1,000)
U S.A.	4,800.0	734.1
U.S.S.R.	1,539.0	—
West Germany	1,150.0	335.0
Japan	38.5	3,050.0
France	1,060.9	380.0
Italy	460.9	108.1
UK	349.9	75.3
India[1]	50.0	1.2
(Punjab)[2]	25.0	—

[1]Inputs to Farm Mechanization, I.S.A.E. publication, 1966.

[2]Some Problems of Mechanization of Agriculture in Punjab, P.A.U. Publication, 1970.

Source: *Farm Machinery Research Corporation*, 20 June 1968 issue.

The trend in American agriculture is towards minimizing labour inputs, not only because of the expense, but because help is simply not available. To reduce labour means increased mechanization. To utilize the machines efficiently requires larger acreages; so farm operational units are increasing in size. Capital requirements to provide land, machinery and livestock are very large. Farming is becoming a business rather than a way of life. Companies are being formed to operate large tracts, sometimes with the previous owners working as employees. This development is still new, but is gradually increasing in popularity. There are at least a dozen large corporate units operating today, mainly in the south-west part of the country. Some of these have stock-holders, have funded debt, hire labour and office staff, sell shares and pay dividends just like the big manufacturing concerns of the country. This type of enterprise may become common in the future.

The results of the changes are spectacular. In 1800 in the U.S.A., 95 per cent of the people lived on farms, fed themselves and the remaining five per cent. Today, about nine per cent live on farms, feed the remaining 91 per cent and produce enough to supply a large export market. More than 90 per cent of the population, freed from the necessity of producing food, can devote their energies to work in factories, in offices, in the professions, and in the service industries. These changes are largely the result, among others, of the invention of the tractor, which is the major contribution of the U.S.A. to world agriculture.

4. Agricultural Revolution of the Twentieth Century in Europe

Chemical Fertilizers and Plant-Protection Chemicals. Apart from tractors, other major factors in increased crop production in the twentieth century are the use of chemical fertilizers and plant-protection chemicals.

Among the nutrient elements essential to plant growth, nitrogen is absorbed from the soil in much larger amounts than any other. Its tremendous supply in the atmosphere as a free, inert gas, has until recently been of no use to non-leguminous plants. Until the beginning of the nineteenth century, nitrogen supply in the soils was replenished by the addition of animal and vegetable wastes. It was only in the early nineteenth century that Chilean nitrate deposits were first mined by the Spaniards. In 1840, Justus Von Liebig, a German chemist, published his famous book, *Organic Chemistry in its Application to Agriculture and Physiology,* which stressed the agricultural significance of the synthesis of nitrogen compounds. Thirty years of tireless chemical and engineering investigations by German researchers demonstrated the feasibility of industrial exploitation of the immense reservoir of free nitrogen in the atmosphere. In 1904, Fritz Haber succeeded in synthesizing ammonia directly from the elements. In 1910, Carl Bosch and A. Mittasch developed a catalyst system and the first pilot plant—a reactor tube—for the synthesis of ammonia. In 1913, the first ammonia synthesis plant, with a capacity to produce a little over 30 tonnes of nitrogen per day, went into operation at Ludwigshafen in Germany. Within 50 years of the installation of this plant, synthetic fertilizer nitrogen accounted for more than 90 per cent of the total world nitrogen production.

Until the last decade, ammonium sulphate, ammonium nitrate, ammonium chloride and calcium nitrate, produced from synthetic or by-product ammonia and corresponding virgin or by-product acids and associated double salts, have been the classic nitrogenous fertilizers. It was in 1922 that urea was first commercially produced from ammonia and carbon dioxide by BASF in Germany. Its use has been gradually increasing because of the economy in its production and handling.

Next to nitrogen, phosphorus is the other nutrient element whose deficiency limits crop growth on farm lands. Animal bones applied to the fields in olden agriculture appear to take care of this need. Phosphorus in the bones is, however, in a relatively insoluble form. Liebig for the first time, in 1840, mooted the idea that the insoluble phosphate in the bones could be rendered water-soluble by treatment with a mineral acid. John Bennet Lawes, an Englishman, treated caprolite— a phosphorus-bearing fossilized dung—with sulphuric acid and established the world's first superphosphate-manufacturing plant in 1842. Since then, phosphate rock reserves have been discovered, extensively mined and acidulated to varying extents in different countries for use as phosphorus fertilizers.

The third fertilizer element, potassium, is generally supplied to the soil as muriate of potash or potassium sulphate. Germany has long been the principal world source of potassium where different potassic minerals—sylvinite, sylvite and carnallite etc.— have been mined from varying depths. With the discovery of extensive potassium reserves in Canada, that country will soon be the leading potassium fertilizer-exporting country in the world. India is singularly deficient in potassium-bearing minerals and has to depend on imports to meet the potassium deficiency of its soils.

Interest in the use of complex fertilizers has been on the increase throughout the world. In India, ammonium phosphates, nitro-phosphates of various grades and NPK mixtures have been distributed during the last few years. In the next few years, di-ammonium phosphate, urea, ammonium phosphate and nitro-phosphates will be the chief complex fertilizers, the last-mentioned in the group being suitable for acidic soils.

Apart from directly resulting in increased crop yields, the use of fertilizers is a potent channel for introducing scientific method and change. Fertilizers give best results with improved seed, good soil, water conservation and proper tillage. Thus the use of fertilizers is an important method of modernizing agriculture and introducing scientific technology in crop production. The agricultural revolution of the twentieth century is largely based upon a more complete understanding of plant nutrition which has led to a greater use of fertilizers.

Plant-Protection Chemicals. Synthetic organic pesticides were used on a very limited scale before World War II. Unsuccessful attempts to synthesize pyrethrum were made during the 1920s but in the 1930s thiocyanates and cyclo-hexylamines, potential pesticides, were synthesized. However, a real breakthrough in pesticide use came with the discovery of Paul Miller of Switzerland in 1939 that DDT, a chemical synthesized in 1874 by Zeidler, was very effective in killing flies, bugs, cockroaches, potato beetle etc. During the Second World War this pesticide was used to kill lice and proved an unprecedented success in halting a typhus epidemic in Italy in 1943-44. BHC was synthesized by Michael Faraday in 1825 but its insecticidal properties were discovered by Dupire and Faucourt of France, and Slade and others of England. In the post-war era, unparalleled benefits were achieved through the use of these two pesticides. These two pesticides were quickly tested against a variety of pests in many lands during 1946-50 and were used on a large scale. Simultaneously, many other organo-chlorine compounds, like chlordane, toxaphene, methoxychlor etc. became available during the 1945-48 period. Of the synthetic organo-phosphatic compounds, TEPP (Tetra ethyl pyrophosphate) was approved in Germany in 1944, although dimefox, another pesticide of this group, was produced in the same country four years earlier. Since the introduction of DDT and BHC as pesticides, a tremendous number of new pesticides have appeared. It is estimated that in the U.S.A. about 900 active pesticidal chemicals formulated into over 60,000 preparations are currently available for use in food production programmes and in programmes relating to public health, animal health, forestry etc.

In the production of pesticides, a beginning was made in India in 1952 when a factory was installed at Calcutta to manufacture BHC. The production of pesticides in India in 1954 was only 432 tonnes and rose to over 26,000 tonnes by 1970. Also, the number of pesticides which are being manufactured in the country has risen to 39. These include insecticides, fungicides, rodenticides and weedicides.

The consumption of pesticides of commercial concentrations in India is only about 28,000 tonnes as against 200,000 tonnes in the U.S.A. although the gross cropped area in the two countries is almost equal; and the figure for Japan is 80,000 tonnes, i.e. about three times that for India even though the gross cropped area of that country is only one-tenth of that of India. On per hectare basis, the pesticide use is only 160 grams in India as against 1,490 grams in the U.S.A., 1,870 grams in Europe and 10,790 grams in Japan.

SECTION II

DEVELOPMENT OF AGRICULTURE IN PUNJAB

5. Punjab

Physical Features, Climate and Crops. Punjab is one of the smaller states of India representing 1.6 per cent of its geographical area, 2.6 per cent of its cropped area and 2.5 per cent of India's population. It is situated in the north-western corner of the country making an international frontier with Pakistan for more than 300 kilometres. It is flanked in the south by Rajasthan and Haryana, in the east by Himachal Pradesh and in the north by Jammu & Kashmir. The history of Punjab goes back to 2500 B.C., the Harappan period, and it has felt the full force of almost every important campaign in northern India. In the last 23 years its territorial extent has been changed thrice. Its boundaries were redrawn at the time of the partition of the country in 1947 when its size was clipped to less than half. Its size increased when Pepsu was merged with it in 1956. In 1966 it was reorganized on a linguistic basis and its area shrank considerably.

The territorial extent of today's Punjab is 29° 30′N to 32° 32′N latitude and 75° 55′E to 76° 50′E longitude. In shape it is roughly triangular with the apex towards the north. The total geographical area of the state is 50,376 square kilometres and its population, according to the census of 1971, is 13.47 million. It has 12,992 revenue estates, 11,947 inhabited villages and 109 towns. Administratively it is divided into 38 tehsils, 11 districts and two provincial divisions.

Geology and Physiography. Punjab's geology has a far-reaching impact on its economy. The plain of Punjab was formed by the deposition of alluvium. It has deep and fertile soils. The alluvium, however, does not hold any promise of minerals of economic importance.

From the geological and physiographic points Punjab is divisible into two regions: the hill region and the plain region.

The Hill Region

This is a small region of the outer range of the Siwalik Hills running along the eastern border of Punjab and is six to ten kilometres in width. The Siwalik Hills are composed of conglomerate, clay and silt—all having the character of fluviatile deposits. The bulk of the material is closely similar to the present-day alluvium of the rivers except that the former is now at a higher elevation and is compact, faulted and folded.

The lithology of the Siwaliks suggests the origin of the sediments as a water-borne debris of the Himalayas. The alternating coarse and fine sediments show that the deposition has been seasonal; coarse and upgraded sediments reveal that it has been carried away by rapidly flowing streams and the similarity of the rock deposits indicates the continuous deposition over a long distance.

The origin of the Siwalik Hills has been explained differently by different geologists. One view is that the present Siwalik range is the flood plain of a big river named Indo-Braham. Many streams from the Himalayas brought down sediments to be deposited in the flood plain of the main river. Another view explains the basis of deposition as a continuous lagoon or fore-deep formed in front of the Himalayan range. The fore-deep came into existence with the uplift of the Himalayas and became the site of deposition of the Siwalik strata which commenced in mid-Miocene. Numerous short streams must have flown into this fore-deep. These streams were fed by the rainfall from the monsoons which were probably set up with the uplift of the Himalayas. The coarser sediments were deposited by the streams during the wet seasons. The cause of the great thickness of strata is that sinking kept pace with the accumulation of sediments and was accelerated by the gradual compression to which the crust was subjected during the period of sedimentation. The sediments so deposited have been elevated and folded during the last series of the Himalayan upheavals.

This low range of the Siwalik Hills separates Una and Sirsa valleys from the plains. The Siwalik region covers the eastern-most area of Punjab and runs like a wall, north-west to south-west, separating Himachal Pradesh from the Punjab plain. The range is broken near Ropar where the river Sutlej comes out in the plain, and near Talwara where the Beas enters the plain. Another break in the range is just east of Garhshanker through which the Nangal-Garhshanker Road passes. The hills are roughly six to ten kilometres in width. The height ranges between 400 and 600 metres in Ropar district and goes up to 725 metres in the northern part of Hoshiarpur. The highest point south of the river Sutlej is 604 metres above sea level whereas in the Hoshiarpur district it is 726 metres above sea level a few kilometres south of Talwara.

The soft rocks of the Siwalik hills with a meagre vegetation cover are severely eroded by the monsoon rains and the region has become an area of very complicated relief.

The Plain Region

More than 90 per cent of Punjab's area is a flat plain, the constituent materials of which are similar to those of the Siwalik Hills. The Punjab plain is a segment of that great Indo-Gangetic plain which is a synclinal basin formed by the elevations of the Himalayas.

The rivers of the region indicate that the plain is the result of a recent deposition and these very rivers have formed it. These rivers have been raising their beds and then breaking through the banks at the time of severe floods to adopt new courses. Within historical times the Sutlej had a very different course from its present one. The same is the case with the Jamuna which once flowed into the Arabian Sea.

All the streams, big and small, issuing from the Siwalik Hills or the Himalayas have deep and narrow channels in their upper courses. As they expand in the open country, their velocity decreases and so also their silt-carrying capacity. Thus the heavier and coarser sediments are deposited immediately out of the hills and only the finer sediments are carried far away. In this way a surface has been formed with a considerable slope near the hills. The surface material is coarse and rough near the Siwalik range but goes on becoming finer away from the hills. The Punjab plain lies between 180 and 320 metres above sea-level. The height is more near the hills and decreases gradually towards the west. In the east a narrow stretch covering most of Ropar and Hoshiarpur districts and Pathankot tehsil lies 300 metres above sea-level. Central Punjab lies between 250 and 300 metres above sea-level. Going further to the west the height continues to decrease and in Fazilka tehsil it is less than 200 metres above sea-level. Near the hills the average slope of the land is more than 18 metres in a kilometre. It decreases to less than four metres in a kilometre about 16 kilometres away from the hills and to less than a metre in a kilometre in the whole of central Punjab. It diminishes to even less than 30 centimetres in a kilometre in the western tehsils of Bhatinda and Ferozepur.

The work of the two important agents of weathering—wind and running water—is well exemplified in this area. The action of wind in the western side and the action of running water near the Siwalik range have changed the face of the plain and have given the different tracts a modified look.

Drainage. Punjab is drained by the rivers Ravi, Beas and Sutlej. Because of their sources in the high snow-clad mountains, these rivers are perennial in character. In the north is the Ravi which flows along the international frontier with Pakistan for about 100 kilometres. The Beas, after flowing for about 130 kilometres in the state, joins the Sutlej well within Punjab. The river Sutlej enters Punjab near Nangal and after flowing for about 230 kilometres through the centre of Punjab separates India from Pakistan for about 100 kilometres in the north-western side and finally enters the Pakistan territory a few kilometres west of Fazilka. All the three are antecedent rivers and have a very uniform slope not only in the plain but in their upper courses also. Throughout the plain the rivers flow in inter-locking channels enclosing islands and sand-bars. The absence of towns and big villages along their banks and the wide extent of their flood plains indicate that floods have been frequent and extensive in the past. The Ghaggar is another river which flows along the southern limits of Punjab. As the source of the river is not in the snow-covered mountains, it is seasonal in character.

The most striking characteristic of the drainage is the presence of scores of seasonal streams in the sub-Siwalik region. They take their rise in the western slopes of the Siwalik Hills. Proceeding away from the hills, the streams begin to unite and take such a course so as to discharge their waters into the big rivers. Many of these, however, do not merge in the big rivers but spread their water over the flat plain. The channels of the streams are very narrow in the hills but expand to the maximum within a few kilometres of them. In the upper reaches their beds are covered with stones, pebbles and coarse sand, but in the plain the beds are covered with sand alone. The streams are completely dry except for a few months of the rainy season. On occasion, when there are heavy rains in the hills and in the adjoining areas, these streams have a formidable amount of rushing water which does a lot of damage in the form of soil erosion.

Climate.   Climatically, Punjab is a sub-humid to semi-arid region. Its latitudinal and continental position has resulted in extremes of temperature conditions. Though the mean daily temperature throughout the year is never below 0°C, yet frost is quite common during winter nights. In summer, on the other hand, day temperatures are very high, exceeding very frequently 45°C. In Ludhiana, a centrally located town of Punjab, the maximum temperature remains above 40°C for 35 days in the year. The highest recorded temperature is 50°C. The maximum number of hottest days of the year is in June. For 35 days in the year the minimum temperature remains below 50°C, and 0°C is the lowest temperature recorded during the month of January. The daily range of temperature over Punjab varies between 8°C and 17°C in the year. The daily range of temperature is minimum during August when the days are hot and humid and nights are warm and muggy. The highest daily range of temperature is during the month of November when the days are warm and nights are cold. The annual range of temperature is 20°C.

The amount of rainfall in Punjab varies from 25 centimetres to more than 100 centimetres, the maximum near the Siwalik

Hills and the minimum in the western side of the state. In the districts of Ropar, Hoshiarpur and Gurdaspur the average annual amount of rainfall is over 80 centimetres. In the central districts of Amritsar, Kapurthala, Jullundur, Ludhiana and Patiala, the amount is 50 to 80 centimetres. In Sangrur, Bhatinda and Ferozepur it is less than 50 centimetres. In the extreme western parts of Ferozepur district the amount of rainfall is about 25 centimetres. Seventy to 80 per cent of the total rainfall is during the three months of July, August and September, when the monsoon winds blow from the south-east; the rest comes during the winter season. The number of rainy days corresponds to the amount of rainfall. About one-third of the total rainy days are during the month of August alone. July and September come next. An important characteristic of the rainfall of this region is that it is highly variable in time as well as in space and the magnitude of the variability corresponds inversely with the amount of rain. As compared to the monsoon rains, the variability of the winter rainfall is 30 to 40 per cent higher throughout Punjab.

The mean relative humidity remains above 75 per cent for more than 30 days in the year. The highest frequency of such days is during the month of August, followed by July and September. On the other hand, the mean relative humidity remains below 30 per cent for 30 to 40 days in the year. The maximum number of days with such low amounts of moisture is during May, followed by April and June.

Land Utilization. The land-use classification data for the year 1968-69 show that 78.38 per cent of the land of Punjab is classified as "net cultivated," 2.27 per cent "forests," 12.67 per cent "not available for cultivation," 2.54 per cent "unculti-vated other than fallows," and 4.14 per cent as "fallow."

A very high proportion of the land is under cultivation because the Punjab plain is free from physical handicaps and deficiency of rainfall has been made up by irrigation facilities. It is only in the districts of Ropar and Hoshiarpur that the cultivated area is less than 60 per cent of the total. It is in these districts that considerable land is covered by the Siwalik Hills and the beds of seasonal streams which cannot be brought under cultivation. Elsewhere in the state, more than 70 per cent of the total land is cultivated. The reason for the small acreage of forests is that Punjab is mostly a flat and fertile plain, more suited for cultivation than for forestry. More than 50 per cent of the forest area of the state is in the districts of Ropar and Gurdaspur, the former alone accounting for 37 per cent of the total. On the other hand, the districts of Ferozepur, Bhatinda, Sangrur, Ludhiana, Kapurthala and Jullundur, which cover 70 per cent of the total area of the state, have less than 30 per cent of the forests of the state. "Land not available for cultivation" covers all such land which is under the hills, beds of rivers and streams, railway lines, roads, canals and buildings. The highest percentage of this category of land is in the districts of Hoshiarpur, Ropar, Gurdaspur and Kapurthala where it is 20 to 34 per cent of the total area, with Hoshiarpur on top, followed by Ropar and Gurdaspur. This high proportion is due to the Siwalik Hills and the numerous seasonal streams. The minimum land covered under this category is in the districts of Ferozepur, Bhatinda and Sangrur, where the amount is only five to six per cent of the total land. The land of this category in these districts is under buildings, roads, railway lines and canals.

The land classified as "uncultivated other than fallows" and areas where additional land could be brought under the plough are very small in the districts of Gurdaspur, Kapurthala, Jullundur and Bhatinda. Ferozepur and Amritsar are the only districts where the extent of this type of land is of any significance. Both these districts collectively account for 50 per cent of the land of this category. The land classified as "fallow," kept uncropped either to maintain fertility or because of a surfeit or deficiency of moisture, is important only in Ferozepur and every year this district alone accounts for one-third or half of the fallow land of the state.

With greater emphasis on the intensive use of land, the pattern of land utilization is rapidly changing and there have been conspicuous changes during the period from 1950-51 to 1968-69. The area under forests has increased from a meagre 19,000 to 114,000 hectares, the net sown area from 3,500,000 to 3,900,000 hectares, the area sown more than once from 626,000 to 1,347,000 hectares and the total cropped area from 4,170,000 to 5,288,000 hectares. On the other hand, the fallow land has shrunk from

445,000 to 208,000 hectares, and uncultivated land other than fallow from 511,000 to 138,000 hectares.

Crop Pattern. Because of favourable physical conditions for crop growth, there is a multiplicity of crops in the state and at any time of the year some crop or other is grown. About three-fifths of the total crops sown are during the winter season, the remaining two-fifths during the summer. Sixty per cent of the crops grown are cereals, eight per cent are pulses, 16 per cent each are cash and fodder crops. The cropping pattern, however, varies a great deal within the state depending upon the availability of moisture and soil conditions.

Wheat, maize, rice and bajra are the important cereals. Wheat dominates not only among the cereals but in the overall crop pattern. About 40 per cent of the annually cropped area of the state is under wheat which accounts for 65 per cent of the area under all the cereal crops. Punjab produces one-fourth of the total wheat of India. So great is the dominance of the crop that in all districts the percentage of the total cropped area under wheat is above 30. The districts of Ludhiana and Jullundur have more than 45 per cent of the cropped area under wheat which occupies about nine per cent of the cropped area. The districts of Jullundur, Hoshiarpur and Ludhiana are more important, whereas its importance in Bhatinda and Ferozepur is somewhat small.

The distribution of rice and bajra, which account for 6.5 per cent and 3.8 per cent of the cropped area of the state, is localized. Rice is an important crop in Gurdaspur, Amritsar, and Kapurthala districts. Elsewhere it is either grown in the flood plains or in the clayey-soil tracts. The minimum acreage under rice is in Bhatinda and the south-western parts of Ferozepur district. Bajra is completely localized in the south-western quadrant of the state and 88 per cent of the state's crop is grown in the districts of Bhatinda, Sangrur and Ferozepur. Among pulses, gram is the outstanding one and covers 6.6 per cent of the cropped area or 80 per cent of the area under all pulses. Seventy-five per cent of the total acreage under the crop is in the districts of Ferozepur, Bhatinda and Sangrur. Cotton, groundnut, sugarcane and potatoes are the principal cash crops of the state.

The distribution of these crops is highly localized.

Cotton leads in this set of crops and covers 7.4 per cent of the cropped area of Punjab. The state contributes about 15 per cent to the total production of the country. Ferozepur and Bhatinda both account for 69 per cent of the cotton area of the state. On the other hand, three eastern districts of Ropar, Hoshiarpur and Gurdaspur account for only 1.5 per cent of the total cotton acreage. Groundnut, with 4.2 per cent of the total cropped area, is the second most important cash crop of Punjab and contributes five per cent to the total groundnut production of India. Ludhiana district and the adjoining tehsils of Patiala, Sangrur and Ropar have 60 per cent of the total acreage of the crop.

Sugarcane covers about three per cent of the cropped area and is mainly grown in the eastern half of the state. Among oilseeds, the dominance is that of rape, mustard and sesamum. The acreage is, however, insignificant as compared to other crops. Rape and mustard are mainly grown in the drier south-western Punjab, whereas 90 per cent of the sesame crop is localized in the districts of Gurdaspur and Amritsar. Fodder crops grown in the state are many and collectively cover one-sixth of the cropped land. Chari, bajra and gowara in summer, and berseem, senji and lucern in winter are the principal fodder crops.

6. The Background

Partition of Punjab and the Rehabilitation of Refugee Agriculturists.
On 15 August 1947 India was partitioned and a new country,
Pakistan, appeared on the map of the world. The brunt of
partition was borne by the state of Punjab which was partitioned
into two segments, the eastern which remained in India, and the
western which was included in Pakistan. West Punjab was
given 16 districts which included 55 per cent of the population
and 62 per cent of the area. It inherited about 69.9 per cent of
the income of the joint province. It also retained about 70 per
cent of the canal-irrigated area, including the famous Canal
Colonies of Lyallpur, Montgomery and Sargodha—the granaries
of India. West Punjab had a population density of a 100 per
square kilometre as compared with 120 in East Punjab and had
crown wastelands which, when provided with irrigation, would
become highly productive. East Punjab had 13 districts and
five princely states. It obtained about 45 per cent of the population, 33 per cent of the area and 31 per cent of the income of the
former united province. It was highly deficit in foodgrains.[1]

The total Hindu and Sikh population of West Punjab in 1941
was about 4.3 million, while the Moslem population of East Punjab
was about 4.2 million. The entire Hindu-Sikh population of
West Punjab had to migrate to India and the same was the case
with the Moslems of East Punjab. It was a refugee problem of
an unprecedented nature in the history of the world. The refugees
came in large columns on foot, in bullock-carts, in trucks and

[1]M.S. Randhawa, *Out of the Ashes*, Chandigarh, 1954, p. 93.

in trains. While the colonists from East Punjab returned to their original villages, the others were given shelter in refugee camps under tents.

The next step was the temporary allotment of land to refugee farmers so that they could sustain themselves. After this the scheme of permanent rehabilitation was taken up. It was a work of vast magnitude and to handle it about 8,000 *patwaris* (revenue officials) were employed. A school building in Jullundur and a township of tents served as a temporary secretariat where this vast staff was accommodated. Punjab had an excellent system of land records and rights of owners were accurately recorded. Exchange of land records was arranged between the East and West Punjab Governments and the land claims of the refugees were verified. By April 1949, the work of verification of claims was completed.

As there was great diversity in soil, irrigation and other factors concerning land in West and East Punjab, the need for evolving a common measure was felt. To meet this demand the concept of a standard acre was evolved. It was a unit for value based on the productivity of land. An acre of land which could yield around 400 kilos of wheat, which was considered the highest yield at that time, was given the value of 16 annas and was termed a standard acre. Land in the Moslem evacuee villages was allotted to the refugee land-owners who had been given temporary allotments of land for cultivation in the alphabetical order of their names. This ensured fairness in allotment.

The Hindu and the Sikh land-holders left an area of 6,700,000 acres in West Pakistan out of which 4,300,000 acres were irrigated while in the East Punjab only 4,700,000 acres were available out of which only 1,300,000 acres were irrigated (Fig. 1). The gap in area of about 2,000,000 acres was met by a scheme of graded cuts. Every land-holder, irrespective of his holdings, was subjected to a cut of 25 per cent and in the case of large land-holders it was as much as 95 per cent. Thus there was a considerable levelling down of land ownership at higher levels.

The calamity of partition provided a great opportunity for schemes for agricultural development and rural renewal. Twenty-seven garden colonies for the cultivation of fruit plants were developed on an area of 20,000 acres. Loans were provided for

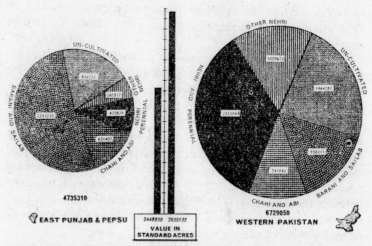

Fig. 1 Evacuee area left by the Moslem land-holders in East Punjab is shown on the left, while the land left by the Sikh and the Hindu land-owners in West Pakistan is shown on the right.

the sinking of tube-wells, purchase of tractors and other agricultural implements. Irrigation by means of tube-wells powered by electricity was promoted for the first time. The use of tractors for cultivation was also an innovation. In fact, modernization of agriculture in the Indian part of Punjab started in 1950 with the rehabilitation of refugees. In the process of land allotment a large number of holdings were consolidated. As the refugee land-owners had more substantial holdings as compared with those of East Punjab, and they were more experienced farmers who were ready to accept innovation, it was they who in due course spearheaded the agricultural revolution.

7. The Human Element

People from Europe who colonized North and South America had the same opportunity to develop the countries which they had adopted as their new homes. Both continents had vast land and water resources, plenty of minerals, and a scanty native population. Yet, it was the people who colonized North America who were more successful. Why was it so? It was because of the human element. The colonists from England and other northern European countries who settled in North America were more hardworking than the Spaniards and the Portuguese who colonized South America.

In India also, as in the rest of the world, the human element has an important role in agricultural development. Kusum Nair, a journalist, travelled all over India from 1958-1960 to assess the role of the human element in rural development. In a number of states she found contentment with the existing miserable conditions. In Punjab alone she saw people who were enterprising and energetic, and she could discover no blossoms in the dust. Even in 1958 she saw humming industries in the towns of Punjab where owners of small workshops were turning out sewing machines, bicycles and agricultural implements in a constant din of hammers and electric motors. She also noticed that the refugee farmers were more progressive and superior in techniques of cultivation to the farmers of East Punjab. She might also have observed that they were not garrulous and preferred to move their hands rather than wag their tongues.

There is no doubt that the Sikh farmer is the best farmer in India. Sikhism is a faith which brought about a social revolution in north India five centuries ago. It broke the fetters of the caste system and provided an equal opportunity to the oppressed and the downtrodden to attain human dignity. It liberated people from the ancient Brahmanical system which looked to the past for its Golden Age. The new faith promoted dignity of labour and exhorted its followers to earn their living by manual work. Its ban on tobacco-smoking promoted physical fitness. Above all, it gave new dignity to agriculture which was declared as the best of professions. The system of the common kitchen which provided free meals also had a levelling influence. The founder of the Sikh religion, Guru Nanak (1469-1539), in his old age settled down at Kartarpur on the Ravi and adopted agriculture as his profession. The surplus production of the farm was contributed to the langar, the common kitchen, where the farm workers and visitors were given free food. Since then the langar has been an essential part of the Sikh faith and no visitor to a Sikh temple who turns up at mealtime is denied free food. It surprises Westerners who visit Punjab, for not even affluent America has such a system of free meals.

The Sikhs are more mobile as compared with other Indian communities, have spread all over India and have even emigrated to many foreign countries. Sizeable numbers of them have settled in California, western Canada, the United Kingdom and Malaya. They are ready to go anywhere in the world where there is opportunity for work and a good wage.

They have many things in common with the Scots; they work hard, are good fighters, and have a passionate love for alcohol. They also have a sense of humour and considerable self-confidence and can enjoy a joke at their own expense. In fact, they have themselves invented most of the jokes current about them. As Dr W.G. Archer observes:

Like Scotsmen, Sikhs have many good qualities—industry, courage, intelligence and tenacity. They indulge at times in outbreaks of berserk frenzy. But they are great fighters and soldiers; they are hard workers and, like the Scots, they have spread all over the globe. Go anywhere and you will find two persons—a Scotsman and a Sikh. Scottish qualities are also reflected in Sikh religion. Its founder, Guru Nanak, is the exact counterpart of John Knox and Sikh worship has a plain simplicity, a quiet suspicion of aesthetic graces that reminds one of Presbyterianism itself. Even in dress, they have the same obsessive need to assert their own identities. The hardened Scot despises coat and trousers and flaunts a kilt, sporran and tam-o'-shanter. A true Sikh wears coat and trousers but faithfully parades a beard and turban. These traits of character have given both peoples a marked individuality.[1]

In dress too they are less conservative and many of them, and particularly the educated, have adopted Western coats and trousers. In fact, out of all the states of India, it is in Punjab that one finds the largest number of people in Western clothes while in the other states the loose multi-purpose dhoti rules supreme.

Theoretically, the caste system is not accepted in Sikhism but division into endogamous groups based on professions persists. The artisans comprising blacksmiths, masons and carpenters are called "Ramgarhias." They are born engineers and have played a vital role in the regeneration of agro-industry in Punjab. By studying foreign designs, they have invented chaff-cutters, threshers, sprayers and seed-cum-fertilizer drills to suit local conditions. They are also pioneers in industry and manufacture electric motors and diesel pumps. Their skill as carpenters and masons is in great demand and they have spread all over India.

The cultivators are Jats, Kambohs and Sainis. They are the best of agriculturists and have great love for land. In fact, agriculture and service in the army are their main professions. They also have aptitude for machinery and easily learn the use of tractors and pump-sets. At the multi-purpose dam sites of India it is these people who handle heavy earth-moving machinery. In a number of states of India the drivers of trucks, lorries and taxis are Sikhs. They colonized the wastelands of West Punjab, Bikaner and Terai. In fact, when one examines the distribution of tractors all over India, their heaviest concentration is in areas colonized by the Sikh farmers.

[1] W.G. Archer, *Paintings of the Sikhs*, London, 1966, p. xviii.

The Canal Colonies of Lyallpur, Montgomery and Surgodha, the so-called Bars in West Punjab, now Pakistan, were colonized by the Sikh Jat farmers and became models of agricultural development. Sir Malcolm Darling, administrator and scholar, who made a deep study of the agricultural population of Punjab, describes the Sikh colonies of Lyallpur thus:

A colony could hardly have had better material, for Ludhiana, Jullundur and Amritsar represent the flower of Indian agriculture. They are the home of the Jat Sikh, who has been described as 'most desirable of colonists'. It would be difficult to say which of the three has produced the best type; for industry and thrift, the Ludhiana Sikh is hard to beat, and the Sikh from Amritsar, though he may be spendthrift and violent, is unsurpassed as a cultivator. Grit, skill in farming, and a fine physique are characteristics common to all, and in his new environment the Jat Sikh has reached a point of development probably beyond anything else of the kind in India. In less than a generation he has made the wilderness blossom like the rose. It is as if the energy of the virgin soil of the *Bar* had passed into his veins and made him almost a part of the forces of nature which he has conquered.[2]

With the spread of modern education, the Sikh farmers and artisans have contributed many men of distinction to the professions and administration. Sikh doctors, engineers and agricultural scientists have contributed significantly to the modernization of Punjab. Most of the scientists of the Punjab Agricultural University have a rural base. That is one reason why their researches are more intimately related to the felt needs of the farmers.

There is another group of people, the Aroras and Khatris who have played a vital role in the regeneration of industry in Punjab. They are highly intelligent and well-educated and form the backbone of the middle class. They have not only contributed writers of distinction and scientific research workers of

---

[*] Sir Malcolm Darling, *The Punjab Peasant in Prosperity and Debt*, Oxford, Bombay, 1947, p. 117.

eminence to the intellectual elite of Punjab, they are also leaders in the fields of commerce and industry. They know the art and science of industrial management and organization. In fact, organized industry in Punjab owes its existence to their wealth and managerial skill.

Driven to India by the partition of the country in August 1947, the Sikh farmers and the Hindu businessmen and entrepreneurs proved a major asset. They are enterprising and accept innovations. They were resettled with speed and during the process of their rehabilitation, agriculture was modernized with loans for sinking tube-wells and for the purchase of tractors, and industry made a remarkable recovery. Credit for this revival goes to the Sikh farmers, blacksmiths and carpenters, and the Hindu entrepreneurs of Punjab. It is their cooperative endeavour in the fields of agriculture and industry which laid the foundations of progress of Punjab.

8. Consolidation of Holdings

As one flies from Calcutta to Amritsar, the rural landscape from Delhi onwards shows a marked change. Instead of irregular fields one sees large areas demarcated into rectangles, with straight roads linking the villages with the fields and the market towns. The number of tube-wells, wells, and homesteads on farms also shows a remarkable increase. How has this happened?

Punjab is an ancient land with cultivation dating to the third millennium B.C. The sites of the Harappan culture—Mohenjo-Daro and Harappa in West Pakistan and Ropar in Indian Punjab—are as old as 2500 B.C. Cultivation near these urban settlements was close to the river-beds. From the river-beds cultivation spread to dry areas with the aid of masonry wells. Considering the long period for which cultivation has been carried on, the increase in population, and the laws of succession one can imagine their combined effect on land holdings.

The laws of succession in India result in the subdivision and fragmentation of holdings. When the father dies, the land is divided equally among all the sons. Each successor insists on having a share from each location which results in further fragmentation. As this process had gone on for several generations, it produced severe fragmentation of land.

Disadvantages of Fragmented and Scattered Holdings. The disadvantages of fragmented and scattered holdings are well known. It is a wasteful method of land utilization and many improved agricultural practices cannot be adopted. A farmer owning three or four acres may have his holding scattered in ten or 15 tiny bits. In some cases the strips of land are so narrow that it is difficult for bullocks to plough them, as sufficient space is not available for easy movement and turning. A good deal of time and energy of the farmer and his bullocks are wasted in moving from one field to another. It has been estimated that expenditure on the cultivation of land increases by 5.3 per cent for every 500 metres of distance for manual labour and ploughing. A good deal of land is wasted in embankments and field boundaries. Canal irrigation is practically an impossibility on scattered plots. A tube-well, or a well cannot be economically sunk. Scattered holdings are also a source of dissension among villagers, who spend their hard-earned money on boundary disputes, and quarrels resulting from cattle trespass. Fencing of scattered pieces of land is an impossibility, and sons of farmers, instead of attending schools, spend their time in preventing cattle trespass. Consequently, large numbers of fragments per holding and their small size resulted in severe under-utilization and wastage of farm resources.

Progress of Consolidation of Holdings in India. The progress of consolidation of holdings in various states of India is given in Table 2.

Table 2
Progress of consolidation of holdings in various states of India

State		Area (thousand hectares). Level achieved—cumulative 1968-69	
Punjab	(Completed)	9,203	(Composite Punjab)
Uttar Pradesh		8,881	
Maharashtra		3,732	
Madhya Pradesh		3,019	
Rajasthan		1,744	
Mysore		1,322	
Gujarat		848	
Andhra Pradesh		337	
Himachal Pradesh		185	
Bihar		71	
Jammu & Kashmir		24	
Assam		2	
West Bengal		—	
Total		**29,368**	

Punjab has a leading position and the entire cultivable area of 9.203 million hectares was consolidated by 1969. The scheme has made least progress in eastern India in the states of Bihar, Assam and West Bengal. These are the problem states of India in which the state of agriculture is deplorable. The scheme is more readily accepted in states with flat land with the minimum number of trees, and where there are more owner-cultivators and fewer tenants. States in which there are large plantations of coconut, areca-nut, rubber, etc., for example Kerala and Tamil Nadu, have little scope. In the hilly areas too consolidation of holdings can be achieved only on a rough exchange basis.

Consolidation of Holdings in Punjab. The work of consolidation of holdings in Punjab was started during the British period in 1920 through cooperative consolidation societies. Since consolidation was voluntary, the progress of the work was very slow and from 1920 to 1951 only 280,000 acres could be consolidated.

Soon after independence, the necessity of consolidation of holdings was realized and the *East Punjab Holdings—Consolidation of Holdings and Fragmentation Act* was enacted in 1948. An element of compulsion was introduced and hence the progress was rapid.

According to this Act, village advisory committees were formed to advise the staff on all matters concerning consolidation of land and in particular in the classification and valuation of fields, and preparation of village consolidation schemes. The preliminary work of the staff was the correction and bringing up-to-date of records of rights and the preparation of preliminary statements. The plots of land were then evaluated, keeping in view the quality of the soil, the source of irrigation, the productivity of land and the distance from the village abadi, etc. The irregular fields were consolidated into rectangular blocks of an acre size.

Apart from consolidating the holdings of the farmers, the scheme provided a unique opportunity for replanning the countryside, which included planning the location of schools, hospitals and roads. Land was also reserved for community buildings, such as community centres, places of worship, and playgrounds. Above all, straight roads were provided to the village abadi as well as to the entire cultivated area. Circular roads around the villages and roads linking one village with another and with the main roads were also demarcated.

The total expenditure on the consolidation of holdings in the composite state of Punjab (including Haryana) was Rs 145,330,000. The cost per hectare of consolidation ranged from Rs 7.42 to Rs 9 which was recovered in full from the beneficiaries, the land-owners. The entire work was completed in 20 years.

A Case Study. A case study was conducted to bring out the

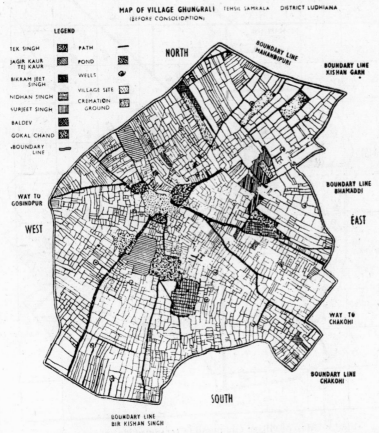

Fig. 2 Map of village Ghungrali (before consolidation).

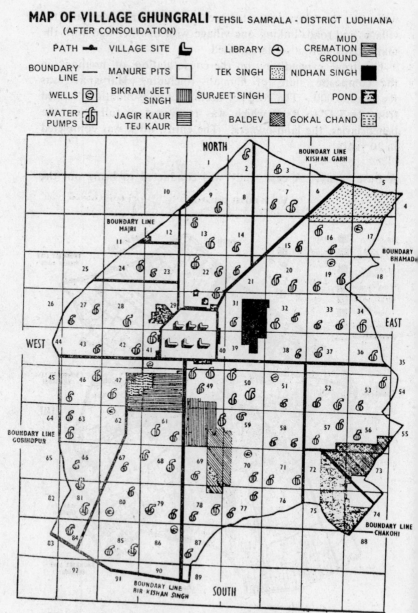

MAP OF VILLAGE GHUNGRALI TEHSIL SAMRALA - DISTRICT LUDHIANA
(AFTER CONSOLIDATION)

PATH ⊷   VILLAGE SITE 凵   LIBRARY ⊖   MUD CREMATION GROUND ▨

BOUNDARY LINE —   MANURE PITS ☐   TEK SINGH ▦   NIDHAN SINGH ■

WELLS ⊖   BIKRAM JEET SINGH ▥   SURJEET SINGH ☐   POND 卍

WATER PUMPS   JAGIR KAUR TEJ KAUR ▤   BALDEV ▨   GOKAL CHAND ▦

Fig. 3   Map of village Ghungrali (after consolidation).

effect of the consolidation of holdings in village Ghungrali of Ludhiana district. Figures 2 and 3 show the difference in the farm situation before and after consolidation in this village. As a result of consolidation of holdings the number of tube-wells in this village increased from four in 1950 to 104 in 1969, and tractors increased from one in 1962 to 16 in 1969. This is true about most of the villages in the state. Any village sample could depict similar differences.

Effect on Agriculture. The most beneficial effect of the scheme of consolidation was that the farmers were enabled to sink tube-wells on their holdings. In 1950 Punjab had no tube-wells. Today, Punjab has 275,000 tube-wells. Besides, there was a considerable reduction in land leased out, which indicates that the owner-cultivators started cultivating their land themselves owing to reduction in the number of fragments. There was also an increase in the cultivated area which was previously lost in embankments. The consolidated plots of land could also enjoy the benefits of canal irrigation. Increase in agricultural production due to consolidation alone without change in techniques was reported to be about 25 per cent.

The only parallel in the history of agriculture which can rival Punjab's consolidation of holdings scheme for its effects on the general life of the people and agricultural production is the eighteenth-century *Enclosures Act* of England. The large land holders absorbed the small holdings of the yeomen and the peasants. "It was radicalism of the rich at the expense of the poor" as Trevelyan remarks. In the Punjab scheme, however, every proprietor of land retained his entire area in one or two blocks irrespective of the fact whether it was large or small.

If Punjab has provided such a sound base for intensive agriculture, particularly for the cultivation of Mexican wheats which require frequent irrigation, it is entirely due to consolidation of holdings. This was achieved on account of sound political and administrative rural-based leadership. The contribution made to the scheme by ministers like Gyani Kartar Singh and Sardar Partap Singh Kairon is by no means small. When the scheme of consolidation of holdings was formulated there was much talk in the air about cooperative and joint farming in which the entire land of a village community as well as their bullocks and implements were to be pooled. "Why go in for a costly and time-consuming process of consolidation of land holdings," some people asked, "when joint or cooperative farming could provide the solution?" Cooperative farming succeeds when there is a well-educated farming community with a business sense, and one whose members are also selfless and angelic. This was not the situation in Punjab. These ideas were tried in a few evacuee villages where refugee farmers were settled and did not succeed anywhere. Cooperation in the supply of inputs and marketing of agricultural produce can be rewarding and has made headway but not in the cultivation of land. The political leadership realized that, instead of building castles in the air, it was better to launch the scheme of consolidation of holdings which was the keenly felt need of the Punjabi farmers who knew that farming was best done by a hardworking family who were bound together by family ties and realized that schemes were no substitute for hard work which people put in with the profit motive which might be ignoble, but it was there and could not be ignored.

9. Land Reforms and Agricultural Development

A sound policy of land reforms is one of the important components of the strategy of Green Revolution. It has two aims: to increase agricultural production and social justice. It has been seen that the best production is obtained in farms which are cultivated by the proprietors themselves and the most inefficient farms are those which are cultivated by tenants. This is mainly due to the fact that tenants have no incentive for land improvement and for the use of chemical fertilizers.

Land is an indispensable input in the agricultural production process. Factor-employment, level and distribution of income and state policy interact within the rest of the agricultural environment through influencing the structure of land holdings. The agricultural production process depends on the system of rights and obligations of the holders of land to its use and there is a close relationship between the land system and the efficiency in agricultural production.

Often the land ownership and use systems lag behind the socio-economic and political objectives of a welfare state, especially when a society changes from a colonial rule to a sovereign and democratic state. This is what happened in India after independence in 1947. Under such a change, land reforms normally involve a rearrangement of ownership and operational rights and other such institutions associated with land. Primarily, any set of land reforms should aim at removing impediments in agricultural production, as they arise from the character of the agrarian structure and secondly create conditions for evolving an agrarian economy with high levels of efficiency and productivity. To what extent these objectives have been achieved through various land reforms made in Punjab that facilitate and accelerate the growth of agricultural development in the state is a pertinent question at this stage. Such an analysis is doubly important because, with 56 per cent of the working force still engaged in agriculture and 61.4 per cent of the state income originating from this primary sector, development of the state economy is heavily dependent upon growth in the agricultural sector.

When the country was partitioned in 1947, Punjab State (then East Punjab, comprising the present Haryana and Punjab and Kangra distirct) had a backlog of serious socio-economic problems. Its economy was shattered, owing to a large-scale destruction of houses and crops. The problem of resettlement of refugees was a formidable one. There was very little industry in the state to absorb any sizable number of refugees. Vast tracts of land were unirrigated, yielding only coarse grains. Agrarian structure was defective in the sense that there existed quite a few intermediaries between the state and the tiller of the soil; tenure was insecure, rents were unregulated and high; holdings were fragmented, and land distribution was so uneven that a small percentage of population owned a large proportion of land, and the majority were either landless or owned uneconomic holdings. As a result, the yield levels were low and agricultural production efficiency was circumscribed by the defective agrarian structure.

In the first instance, Punjab being a deficit state at that time, there was a need for increasing agricultural production. Secondly, the Government of India aimed at establishing a just society free from exploitation. Some land reforms were, therefore, introduced in the state consistent with the political objectives of a socialistic democracy.

Since most of the legislations were passed in the early fifties and at that time the present Punjab area was composed of parts of two states (erstwhile Punjab and erstwhile Pepsu), there exist at present two sets of Acts applicable to these areas. The following major legislative Acts are operative at present: *East Punjab Utilization of Land Act, 1949; The Punjab Occupancy Tenants (yesting of proprietary rights) Act, 1952; The Punjab*

Abolition of Ala-Malkiyat and Talukdari Rights Act (*Punjab Act IX of* 1953); *The Punjab Security of Land Tenures Act,* 1953; *Patiala and East Punjab States Union Abolition of Biswedari Ordinance,* 2006 *B.K.* and *The PEPSU Tenancy and Agricultural Lands Act,* 1955.

These Acts and the abolition of intermediaries, tenancy reforms and ceilings on holdings have placed a large number of cultivators in a direct relationship with the state. All *Jagirs* (except war *Jagirs*) were abolished in Punjab and occupancy tenants were given permanent rights. With the fixation of an upper limit of land that can be resumed for self-cultivation, an area of 177,796 acres was declared surplus up to 30 September 1970. As a result, 26,088 eligible tenants were settled on 63,422 standard acres. Some 20,910 standard acres and 1,936 ordinary acres have been purchased by landless tenants. About 98 per cent of the cases involving surplus area have been decided and 66 per cent of the surplus area has been used for the resettlement of eligible tenants.

As a result of these measures the area cultivated by owners increased from 51.4 per cent of the total in 1947 to 66.4 per cent in 1957 and 80.89 per cent in 1969-70. Area cultivated by tenants, on the other hand, decreased from 47.2 per cent in 1947 to 32.5 per cent in 1957 and to 19.11 per cent in 1969-70. Area operated by occupancy tenants declined from 9.9 per cent to 4.6 per cent in 1957 and to zero by the end of the fifties. This was due to the fact that 647,740 occupancy tenants acquired proprietary rights over an area of 1,850,489 acres. Although there existed some exemptions from the ceilings for gardens, mechanized and well-managed farms, Punjab as a result of these measures emerged as a land of peasant proprietors.

A stable and restructured rural base with an equitable tenurial system thus paved the way for the Green Revolution and can be accredited with its blooming to the present state. It created a highly responsive agricultural and rural society which had capacity and was willing to adopt and absorb the elements of improved production technology.

It may, however, be pointed out that land reforms are only one factor, although a very important factor, in the efficient operation of the farm economy. It should not be considered the only string to play upon at all times and under all circumstances. Whereas land reforms have provided a healthy change in the structure of the rural economy, overplaying of this aspect might do more harm than good in future. There is a serious debate going on at present in the country on the lowering of ceilings on land holdings. Since this was included in the manifesto of the Congress Party and this party is now a ruling party, various states are passing legislations to lower the ceiling to between ten and 18 acres of irrigated land. The step seems to be consistent with the political commitments and looks attractive from the point of view of social justice. There are no opinions that certain exemptions above the present ceilings do not stand the test of economic, social and political objectives of this society, yet it is doubtful if lowering of the ceilings *per se* will be in the interest of society in the long run.

Equitable distribution of productive assets and the accompanying economic power are a plausible solution to the socio-economic polarization problems of a democratic society, yet overdone, it can do more harm than good. Distribution of productive assets (land in this case) should not after all be considered the only and universal solution to all the problems of a society. If redistribution assumes the shape of a process of atomization of land holdings, there will be little scope for the introduction of elements of modernization and improved production technology. A downward spiral or a vicious circle of low productivity and poverty distributed among ever-increasing numbers will set in. Making the realtively well-off section of society poorer, to equate it with the poor without making the poor tangibly better-off, is no solution to general poverty. It will be a low-keyed, rather misdirected implementation of the "*Garibi Hatao*" programme.

At this stage of economic growth and development in India, an overriding national objective should be the enhancement of agricultural production, mobilization of agricultural surpluses (marketed surpluses), encouragement of the intersectoral capital flow from the agricultural to the non-agricultural sector in order to create more non-farm gainful employment opportunities. Farm size, productivity, flow of agricultural surpluses, employment within agriculture and the capacity of the agricultural sector to stimulate employment-creation in the non-farm sector are intimately linked up. A dispassionate and objective analysis of the situation in Punjab shows that at this stage ceilings on land holdings up to 30 standard acres put an appropriate limit on farm size from the point of view of economic efficiency, social justice and employment of farm labour. A set of policies, economic and social, to encourage land holdings around this size seems to be in order with a view to maximizing production and marketed surplus per unit of land. Exemptions to hold land above these ceilings do not meet the criteria of economic efficiency and social justice. Lowering of the level of ceilings at the existing level of production technology does not seem to meet the test of economic efficiency and is not very certain to expand overall employment because the level of additional employment (or prevented unemployment) can get offset by a reduction in production, marketed surplus and capital outflow, correspondingly reducing the level of employment in the non-farm sector.

It must not be forgotten that apart from chemical fertilizers, tractors are playing a great role in modern agriculture. For efficient cultivation of land and placement of fertilizers they are a *must* in intensive agriculture. In the threshing of wheat they are playing a heroic role. Unlike combines they also make bhoosa. With double-cropping the land is to be cleared quickly by harvesting the wheat crop and preparing it for the kharif crops. This is only possible with the use of machinery, particularly tractors. There is little doubt that, if under passions of politics, the area is reduced to a level so that mechanized cultivation becomes impossible, it would also lead to a diminution in production and ultimately to a reduction in the food surplus.

Those who advocate a drastic reduction in land holdings by lowering the ceiling often give the argument that cooperative farming can provide the substitute for individual cultivation. My experience of agriculture over the whole of India shows that nowhere has cooperation in cultivation succeeded. Even in socialist countries like Poland and Yugoslavia, where private farms are permitted, they are more productive than state farms. Undoubtedly, cooperation is beneficial in the marketing of produce and in that field it has been a success. Farmers are strong individualists and they prefer to cultivate land according to their capabilities. They dislike any interference.

The advocates of small holdings point to Japan as their ideal. Japan is a densely populated rice-growing country which is mostly hilly. It cannot be compared with the flat wheat lands of Punjab and Haryana where more land per head is available. The farmers of Japan have made a success because government policies are incentive-oriented, price of fertilizers is low, tractors and farm machinery are easily available and agriculture is heavily subsidized. Besides, their farms are linked with the prosperous markets of Tokyo and other large industrial cities. At present, however, no part of India is like Japan. If any foreign country can serve as a model for Punjab and Haryana, it is Denmark. In that country, the average size of farms is about 40 acres.

Even in the Soviet Union, where large-scale mechanization has been done by organizing state farms which are well-equipped with machinery, 67 per cent of the total quantity of potatoes produced, 37 per cent of vegetables, 35 per cent of meat, 37 per cent of milk, and 54 per cent of eggs, are raised in private plots allotted to members of the state farms. Moreover, the size of the country is vast and population relatively small and that is why large mechanized farms seem to be a necessity.

In the matter of ceilings, one can also not forget the problem of rural-urban parity. Punjab and Haryana are the only states in which the gap between the rural and the urban people is narrowest and education has made progress in the rural area as well. Hence the present Punjab Government when it decided that in the matter of ceilings, the ceiling in the urban and the rural sectors should be at par, it was only reflecting the feelings of a large number of rural people who are no longer backward and who do not want to become backward.

One can also not forget the class and caste war between the agriculturists and the urban middle classes. It is only now that the agriculturists are coming up in the field of education and are proving serious competitors to their former exploiters, who lose no opportunity in damaging their rivals and are gleefully contemplating their economic ruin. They do not realize that in the process they may harm the urban working classes.

No doubt, the various components of land reforms so far have provided a responsive rural structure for the absorption of improved production technology in the past, yet the current attempts to lower the ceilings below 30 acres need to be moderated with economic logic and overall long-range social considerations. In a socialistic democracy, political decisions, to be appropriate, must be based on economic logic and social considerations in the long run. It would be unfortunate if political expedients take precedence over hard economic realities to look not far beyond the nose in respect of social problems of polarization and unemployment.

SECTION III

GREEN REVOLUTION IN PUNJAB

(i) Services to Support Agricultural Development

The State of Punjab has built up a system of services to support agricultural development. Initiative for most of these was provided by the Government of India. Briefly, these are the Development Department which includes the departments of Agriculture and Animal Husbandry, an extension agency with the Development Commissioner at the state level, and the village level worker at the village level, the Punjab Agricultural University which provides a base for education, research and extension; and the Cooperative Department which provides credit to the farmers. Besides these there are autonomous organizations supported by the State Government e.g. the Punjab State Cooperative Supply and Marketing Federation, and the Agro-Industries Corporation which supply fertilizers, tractors and other farm machinery to the farmers. In the following chapters, a brief account is given of these organizations and their functions.

10. Agriculture and Development Departments

Close collaboration between the Punjab Agricultural University and the State Department of Agriculture has played a major role in increasing agricultural production in Punjab. A large number of other institutions have also made significant contributions in educating the farmers in the new technology. The role of some of these institutions is described below.

Development Departments of the State Government. Before the inception of the agricultural universities and the launching of the national extension service and community development programmes, the entire work of teaching, research and extension in agriculture was handled by the State Department of Agriculture. The extension workers of the department in the rural areas—Agricultural Inspectors, District Agricultural Officers and Deputy Directors—promoted new techniques among the farmers. However, considering the size of the problem and inadequacy of staff, their efforts did not make a sizable impact.

The Development Department with a Development Commissioner as the leader and coordinator of agricultural development schemes, came into existence in 1952. Village level workers were provided at the village level to guide the farmers and they played an important role in making the farmers turn from traditional to scientific agriculture. The District Development and Panchayat Officer acts as a coordinator of all activities of the Agriculture Department with other departments operating at the district level. The overall responsibility at the district level lies with the Deputy Commissioner who controls the work of Block Development and Panchayat Officers and Agricultural Extension Officers. The Development Department has rationally channelled and systematized all efforts at agricultural development from the village to the state level.

Though with the inception of the Punjab Agricultural University in 1962, responsibility for teaching and research and partly that for extension has been shifted to the University, yet the Departments of Agriculture and Development are still doing a great deal in educating the farmer. Multiplication of seeds of improved crop varieties evolved by the Punjab Agricultural University is also being carried on by the Department of Agriculture.

Panchayats. A panchayat is an elected statutory body at the village level elected by the adult members of a village. In addition to their judicial, civic and administrative functions, panchayats help in increasing agricultural production. Primarily, the panchayats provide a liaison between the extension agencies and the rural population. There are many instances, where sarpanches helped agricultural extension workers by introducing them to the villagers, by providing facilities to hold meetings and demonstrations and also by providing them with board and lodging during their visits. The scheme of disseminating agricultural information through radio-sets maintained by the panchayats has also made a contribution to the campaigns for greater agricultural production.

Gramsewaks' Training Centres. Since the village-level worker or the gramsewak is a key worker in all development programmes, his proper training is necessary for the success of community development programmes. This duty is performed by the gramsewak training centres which equip the trainees with scientific agricultural technology and extension-education methods. Both the pre-service and in-service training courses for village level workers are being organized at these centres. The gramsewaks trained at these centres are generally successful in discharging their duties. To impart practical training to the trainees, the surrounding agricultural areas are treated as laboratories. The agricultural development of these areas, therefore, owes a lot to the existence of these training centres.

Khalsa College and the Farmers' Training Centre, Amritsar.
Khalsa College, Amritsar has trained many agricultural graduates.
Although after the opening of the Punjab Agricultural University
in 1962, all teaching and research work previously carried out
under the auspices of the Panjab University was transferred
to the Punjab Agricultural University. Khalsa College, Amritsar,
has continued to impart agricultural education under affiliation
to the Panjab University.

A farmers' training programme was started at the Khalsa
College in 1969 under the auspices of the Ministry of Food,
Agriculture, Community Development and Cooperation. This
scheme, working under the high-yielding varieties programme,
is concerned with mainly two types of activities—institutional
training and field training. Under institutional training,
courses varying in duration from a week to three months are
organized for the farmers. Young farmers' training courses,
specialized courses for farmers in animal husbandry, poultry,
vegetables and fruit production, bee-keeping, farm machinery
and crop husbandry, and farm women's courses are held at
the headquarters of the training centre.

The second activity includes the organization of result-and-
method demonstrations at the farmers' fields, production-cum-
demonstration camps of one day duration and farmers' discussion
groups. These activities go a long way in educating the farmers
in the right use of scientific technology.

Rural Schools. Schools in the rural area have helped by
preparing the youth to take up farming as a profession and also
to go in for higher education in agriculture. With greater
stress on the introduction of agriculture as a subject in high and
higher secondary schools, more and more farmers' sons are
getting interested in farming. The boys studying agriculture in
schools transmit their knowledge to their parents. The school-
teacher, being in close contact with the farmers, enjoys their
confidence and promotes the adoption of new technology.

Private Industrial Organizations. Many private companies
engaged in the manufacture of pesticides, insecticides, fertilizers,
weedicides and agricultural machinery also popularize their

use. Such companies have field agencies which educate the farmers in the proper use of their products. Frequent method-and-result demonstrations are conducted by them. Some organizations are even advancing loans to the farmers to help improve farm techniques and also provide fellowships to research scholars.

All India Radio. The farm and home broadcasting unit of All India Radio, Jullundur, started functioning in April 1966. The object of setting up this unit was to collect interesting material by taking the mike to the fields, where actual agricultural work is being done and to interview farmers in their natural surroundings. This was necessary to ensure authenticity and introduce realism into the programme. This unit has been working in close cooperation with the Intensive Agricultural Development Programme, Ludhiana, Punjab Agricultural University, including the district level specialists, and the state departments of Agriculture, Animal Husbandry and Community Development. In this way, it has been able to provide active educational support and timely information to the farmers. It also maintains liaison with the research stations, training centres and progressive farmers of the region in programme planning and projection.

The agricultural programmes are broadcast daily thrice—*Kheti Bari* (Agriculture) is a morning service for five minutes from 6.45 to 6.50 A.M. in the summer, and 7.20 to 7.25 A.M. in the winter. *Unnat Kheti* (Progressive Farming) is a midday service, from 2.00 to 2.10 P.M. and *Khet Khalwar* (Field and the threshing floor) is a half-hour evening service from 7.15 to 7.45 P.M. The evening programme includes features, interviews, discussions, talks by specialists and farm news.

This service highlights the seasonal requirements of farmers by way of seeds, fertilizers and pesticides. Experts from the research institutions inform the listeners about crop raising through lively dialogues interspersed with folk songs. Announcements of market rates of agricultural produce are a regular feature of this programme. In the other two programmes, *Kheti Bari* and *Unnat Kheti*, hints pertaining to day-to-day field operations are given. These hints and the seasonal forecasts and timely information on frost, insect pests, crop diseases, etc. are linked together.

Twice a week, on Tuesdays and Fridays, the half-hour *Khet Khalwar* programme is devoted to features of special interest to farmers who are members of the radio rural forums. The queries received from the various forums about improved seeds and methods of cultivation are answered.

11. The Punjab Agricultural University and Mexican Dwarf Wheats

In the development of agriculture, the Punjab Agricultural University has a pivotal role. The impact of this young institution on the economy of the state is widely recognized and has been far more spectacular than perhaps anticipated in 1962 when it came into being. It was established with the objective of developing a programme which could contribute to increased agricultural production and improvement of the cultivators' economic status. By devoted service to the farming community through meaningful agricultural education, scientific research and extension education it has fulfilled the expectations of the people. The work in the university has brought about a real revolution in farming techniques and it has also had an impact on the attitude of the farmers and the policies of the State Government. It has been a revolution from pessimism, conservatism and age-old traditions to innovations, dashing adventurism and hope. The brief history of this institution is a record of significant achievements and the future is full of promise.

Historical Background. The idea of establishing agricultural universities in India originated with the report of the Indian University Education Commission, 1948-49, popularly called the Radhakrishan Report, followed by the recommendations of the first and second Indo-American teams in 1955 and 1960 respectively. Dr M.S. Randhawa, the present Vice-Chancellor of the Punjab Agricultural University was the chairman of the second team whose report gave final shape to this idea.

The translation of this idea into practice in Punjab was supported by the Cummings' Committee Report of 1960 and the earlier proposal for the establishment of a rural university in Punjab submitted by the T.C.M. team under the leadership of Dr T.S. Sutton in collaboration with the faculty of the College of Agriculture at Ludhiana in 1957. The progressive leadership of Sardar Pratap Singh Kairon, the then Chief Minister of Punjab, and his vision to convert the State of Punjab into the California (where he had received his education) of India helped in the quick adoption of the idea.

The main idea behind the establishment of the agricultural university was to bring about an integration of teaching, research and extension education programmes in agriculture and allied fields at one institution to accelerate the development of the rural economy in the state. To ensure efficiency and rapidity of development, the second Indo-American team had suggested that (i) the agricultural universities should be autonomous in status; (ii) their various constituent colleges such as the College of Agriculture, Veterinary Medicine, Animal Husbandry, Home Science, Basic Sciences and Humanities, Agricultural Engineering etc. be located on one campus; and (iii) there should be integration in teaching, research and extension. All these recommendations were readily accepted by Sardar Kairon and a decision to transfer the entire teaching, research and extension education in agriculture and allied fields to the University was immediately implemented.

The University has been fortunate in the leadership it got. The first Vice-Chancellor, Dr P.N. Thapar, a senior member of the I.C.S., was a very capable administrator. He had been closely associated with the agricultural development of the state and the country and had been Secretary of the Union Ministry of Food and Agriculture.

Dr Thapar remained Vice-Chancellor for about six years and the period of his administration is remembered for excellent traditions and high standards set for recruitment of faculty members. On Dr Thapar's retirement, Dr M.S. Randhawa who had a very long association with the agricultural development of the country, succeeded him. He took over as Vice-Chancellor in October 1968. Like his predecessor, Dr Randhawa is also a very senior member of the Indian Civil Service and has a rare combination of qualities. He has a long record of promotion of agricultural sciences having served with distinction as Secretary and later as Vice-Chairman of the Indian Council of Agricultural Research. He not only commands great respect in the country's scientific and intellectual circles but is also greatly respected by the farming community in the state who look up to him as their great benefactor and well-wisher. Under his leadership the University is developing rapidly in all spheres and has become a centre of excellence for agricultural education and research.

The right choice of executive heads for this institution has been a very big factor in its success.

Set-up. The University's highest administrative body, the Board of Management, has control over the finances and assets of the institution and it provides overall guidance on its running. The Board is presided over by the Vice-Chancellor and has as its members the Chief Secretary and Secretaries, Finance and Agriculture of the State Government; the Directors of the Departments of Agriculture and Animal Husbandry, a representative of the Indian Council of Agricultural Research, two eminent agricultural scientists, two progressive farmers, an industrialist or businessman associated with agricultural development and a woman social worker. The University's Registrar is the Secretary of the Board. The Vice-Chancellor is the chief executive officer of the University.

There are five constituent colleges of the University, all located on the main campus at Ludhiana. These are the Colleges of Agriculture, Basic Sciences and Humanities, Agricultural Engineering, Home Science and Veterinary Medicine. Each college is headed by a dean. There is a University-wide directorate of research and a directorate of extension education. The Dean, Postgraduate Studies, heads the University's postgraduate teaching programmes. The organizational set-up for teaching, research and extension education is shown in Table 3.

Table 3

Chancellor

Vice-Chancellor

Director of Extension Education	Deans of the Constituent Colleges			Director of Research
College of Agriculture	College of Basic Sciences and Humanities	College of Agricultural Engineering	College of Home Science	College of Veterinary Medicine
1. Plant Breeding	Chemistry & Biochemistry	Agricultural Engineering	Food & Nutrition	Physiology
2. Horticulture	Economics & Rural Sociology	Civil Engineering	Textile and Clothing	Surgery and Gynaecology
3. Extension	Mathematics and Statistics	Mechanical Engineering	Home Management	Medicine and Clinics
4. Soil Sciences	Microbiology	Electrical Engineering	Home Science Extension Education	Anatomy
5. Agronomy	Genetics	—	Child Development	Disease Investigation and Bacteriology
6. *Botany & Plant Pathology	Languages	—	—	Parasitology and Bacteriology
7. *Zoology & Entomology	History	—	—	—
8. Food Science and Technology	Journalism	—	—	—
9. Animal Science	—	—	—	—

*The Botany and Zoology Sections of these departments form part of the College of Basic Sciences and Humanities.

There are 30 departments in the five constituent colleges. The degree programmes offered by the University and the students enrolled for the year 1970-71 is as under:

Table 4

B. Sc. (Agriculture)	1,002
B. Sc. (Honours)	50
B. Sc. (Home Science)	189
B. V. Sc. & Animal Husbandry	123
B. Sc. (Agricultural Engineering)	193
M. Sc.	362
Ph. D.	106
Total	**2,025**

In addition to degree courses, the University offers short-duration courses and training programmes to farmers, extension workers, bank employees, housewives, etc. in the areas of their interest. The University maintains a close liaison with the State Department of Agriculture, Animal Husbandry, Fisheries, etc.

The main source of financial support to the University is an annual grant from the State Government. Grants from agencies like the Indian Council of Agricultural Research, the Government of India, PL-480, are also received. The total budget of the University for 1970-71 depicts the sources of finance as given below:

Table 5

Total budget of the University for 1970-71 and its break-up

	Sources	*Millions of rupees*
1.	Punjab State schemes	24.56
2.	I.C.A.R.	2.87
3.	PL-480	0.25
4.	Central Government-sponsored schemes	0.40
5.	Ford Foundation schemes	0.29
6.	Atomic Energy schemes	0.06
7.	Schemes to be financed out of their income	0.44
8.	Schemes financed by other agencies	1.00
	Total	**29.87**

The University has an estate of 1,203 acres at the main campus at Ludhiana, out of which an area of 463 acres is under roads and buildings and the remaining 740 acres constitute the research farm. For research work on regional problems the University has four regional research stations and four regional substations as detailed below. It also has a seed farm for the multiplication and supply of nucleus seeds of improved crop varieties.

Table 6

		Area in acres
1.	*Regional Research Stations*	
	(i) Abohar	207.5
	(ii) Gurdaspur	233.5
	(iii) Kapurthala	305.5
	(iv) Jullundur	232.0
2.	*Regional Research Substations*	
	(i) Kheri (Sangrur)	101.0
	(ii) Bahadurgarh (Patiala)	51.88
	(iii) Samrala (Ludhiana)	31.0
	(iv) Faridkot (Bhatinda)	158 6
3.	*Nucleus Seed Production Farm*	
	Naraingarh (Patiala)	385.6
	Total	**1,740.1**

The University has a well-developed information and communication organization. It holds two farmers' fairs every year—one before the sowing of summer crops and the other before the sowing of winter crops. Thousands of farmers visit the University on these days to see the work in progress to acquaint themselves with the latest findings, and to discuss their problems with the experts. Even though the staff of the University's Extension Education Department remain in constant touch with the farmers and other extension agencies, yet these farmers' fairs constitute an excellent extension link between the University and the cultivators.

Collaboration with U.S. Institutions. The P.A.U. has been assisted in its establishment by the Ohio State University through the Agency for International Development and by the Ford Foundation. The Ford Foundation has made a significant contribution to the establishment of the College of Agricultural Engineering. The greatest contribution made by the Ohio State University is the training of the members of the faculty with the result that the P.A.U. has been able to maintain a high standard of recruitment. These well-trained scientists have played an important role in disseminating new technology. Specialists from the U.S. universities serving with their Indian counterparts have also helped to improve the standards of teaching, research and extension education.

Contribution to date. In the short period of eight years the P.A.U. has made a significant contribution to improvements in agricultural technology which have made this small state the granary of India. Not only has agricultural production considerably increased, thus bettering the lot of the farming community, but the general economy of the state has received a big boost. The dream of the University's founder to develop Punjab as the most progressive state in India is coming true, as the following account will reveal:

(a) Wheat Revolution

The Green Revolution in Punjab is essentially a revolution in wheat-production technology which has led to an abundance and self-sufficiency in food from chronic shortage and dependence on heavy imports. The speed with which Indian scientists have achieved this has hardly ever been witnessed anywhere else in the world. Even Mexico, where dwarf wheats were introduced earlier, needed 15 years to do what Punjab has done in five years.

While this achievement has received wide publicity the efforts that led to it are not as well known. It is also not realized that this so-called revolution has only temporarily eased the country's food situation. For permanent relief the present gains will have to be consolidated and continued efforts for similar future improvements will be needed not only in wheat but in other foodgrains as well as commercial crops.

In the thirties commendable wheat-breeding work was done by Dr Ram Dhan Singh at the Agricultural College and Research Institute, Lyallpur. As a result of his efforts wheat varieties like C 518, C 591, C 228, C 217 and C 250 were evolved. Two varieties, C 518 and C 591, made a great impact on wheat production. However, the genetic potential of these tall wheat varieties was limited and their yields under ideal conditions of cultivation rarely went beyond 30 quintals per hectare. The averages were much lower. After the establishment of the P.A.U., an excellent variety of tall wheat, C 306, was released in 1965. It has a very good grain quality with a yield potential about 30 per cent higher than C 518 and C 591. It proved to be the highest-yielding tall wheat variety not only in Punjab but also in Haryana, U.P., Rajasthan and Bihar. However, the real breakthrough came with the import of dwarf wheat varieties from Mexico, followed by rapid local selections therefrom, and the speedy expansion of their cultivation with matching and needed agronomic improvements suggested by the P.A.U. scientists.

It was in 1963 that about 150 strains of dwarf wheats were received in India from Dr E.N. Borlaug in Mexico. They were distributed among wheat-breeders in Ludhiana, Delhi and Kanpur. The Plant-Breeding Department of the P.A.U. under the leadership of Dr D.S. Athwal selected two promising strains, V 18 and S 227, from them and multiplied their seed at Keylong in 1964. The V 18 was designated as PV 18 and it gave an average yield of 4,690 kilograms per hectare relative to 3,291 kilograms per hectare of C 306—the best local wheat variety at that time. The highest yield obtained from PV 18 from one plot in Ludhiana was 6,914 kilograms per hectare. The strain S 227 was still segregating and further selections were made from it for rust resistance, amber grain colour and grain size. This led to the development of Kalyan-Sona 227 and of Sonalika (S 308) which has an amber colour and bold grain. The variety Kalyan-Sona 227 has amber grain and its yield potential is as good as that of PV 18.

With the selection of these three Mexican wheat varieties the P.A.U.'s scientists made efforts to rapidly multiply the seeds of these selections by raising a second summer crop in the Lahaul Valley. This strategy led to quick seed-multiplication and speedy expansion of area under these varieties.

Kalyan-Sona 227 is at present the most important wheat variety in Punjab. Like PV 18 it is a two-gene dwarf and is highly fertilizer-responsive. It has a yield potential of well over 60 quintals per hectare.

The following details show the rapid increase in wheat

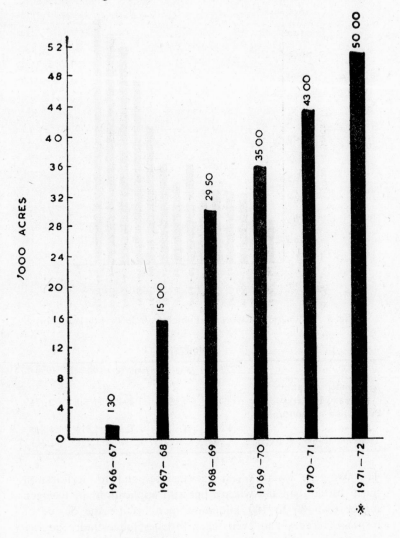

Fig. 4 Acreage under high-yielding wheat varieties in Punjab.

production and yield brought about by the new wheat technology (Figs. 4 and 5).

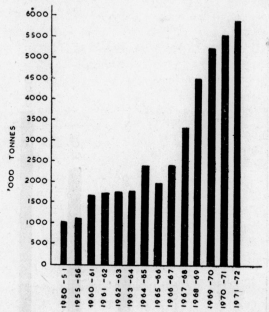

Fig. 5   Production of wheat in Punjab from 1950-51 to 1971-72.

Table 7

	1950-51	1955-56	1960-61	1965-66	1969-70
Area under wheat in thousand hectares	1,137	1,292	1,394	1,548	2,111
Production in thousand tonnes	1,024	1,136	1,725	1,916	4,800
Yield kilograms per hectare	901	879	1,237	1,238	2,243

The two-gene dwarf wheat varieties respond to fertilization much better than tall wheats, but with applications of nitrogen higher than 80 to 100 kilograms per hectare the degree of response recedes and even these varieties lodge under heavier fertilization.   More fertilizer-responsive genetic stocks are therefore needed for higher yields.   Further, Kalyan-Sona is progressively becoming susceptible to brown rust.   The P.A.U.'s plant-breeders are therefore evolving more fertilizer-responsive and disease-resistant varieties. The three-gene dwarfs which have still shorter plants than those of the two-gene dwarfs are being tested. These have a thicker straw, and with higher levels of fertilization are capable of yielding more. A three-gene dwarf variety of wheat (WL 212) evolved at Ludhiana is under advanced stages of testing. It has outyielded Kalyan-Sona 227 by a margin of about ten per cent on an average in various trials and holds great promise. Still better strains with better grain quality are in hand. A couple of two-gene dwarf varieties, WG 377 and WG 357, with good yield potentials and excellent grain quality are also under advanced trials.

These new wheat varieties, with improved crop agronomy that the agronomists have standardized through strenuous experimentation, should not only stabilize the gains of the wheat revolution but lead to further improvement in wheat production.

(b) Rice Revolution in the Offing

There have been significant achievements in the P.A.U.'s rice-breeding programme over the past five or six years. The dwarf rice varieties like IR 8 and Jaya have yielded at several locations in the state more than ten tonnes per hectare in 140 to 145 days from seed to seed. At well-maintained farms their average yield has been well over 60 quintals per hectare.

New dwarf rice varieties with good yield potentials and short-duration ripening are also in advanced stages of testing. A new variety, IR 579, is capable of yielding 70 quintals per hectare of good quality rice in 120 to 125 days. A mutant, 95, takes 90 to 95 days from seed to seed and has a yield potential of about 60 quintals per hectare. These short-duration varieties are expected to fit in with situations where long-duration varieties cannot be grown.

With the availability of high-yielding rice varieties the farmers are bringing more area under rice (Figs. 6 and 7). Areas not traditionally considered suitable are being put under this crop. The production of rice in the state has increased from 0.29 million tonnes in 1965-66 to about 0.6 million tonnes in 1970—an increase of over 100 per cent. With the likely release of short-duration varieties in the next two or three years the

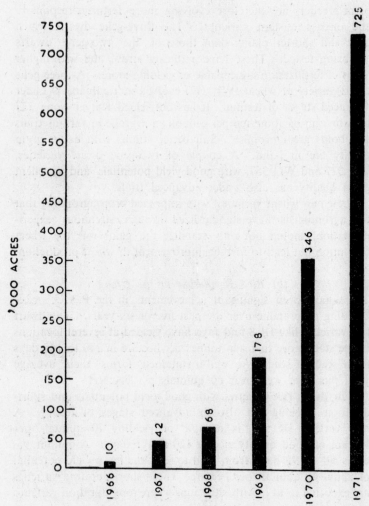

Fig. 6   Acreage under high-yielding rice varieties in Punjab.

area under rice and yield per unit area are likely to increase rapidly as it will not only be possible to obtain heavy yields from the crop but also to fit into the multiple-cropping pattern.

(c) Hybrid Bajra

The evolvement and spread of HB 1, a hybrid bajra, *Pennisetum*

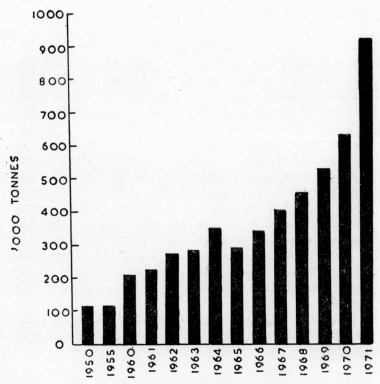

Fig. 7   Production of rice in Punjab.

typhoides (an important millet grown in several states of India), is a very important contribution made by the P.A.U. Evolved by crossing an imported male-sterile line (CMS 23A) from the U.S.A. with an inbred line (BIL 3B) developed at Ludhiana, this variety is capable of yielding 60 to 100 per cent more under rain-fed and irrigated conditions respectively than the previously approved varieties. This variety has done well all over India. This was the first hybrid variety of bajra evolved in India or abroad and its evolvement earned a great deal of acclaim for the P.A.U. from scientists and farmers in the country.

With the introduction of hybrid bajra the yield of this millet increased from 381 kilograms per hectare in 1965-66 to 1,055 kilograms in 1968-69. The area under bajra in Punjab is limited. The improvement in this millet has been of great benefit to the farmers of the dry region.

(d) Moong G 65

Though pulses form an important component of the Indian diet, very little research has been conducted on them. The yields of most pulse crops are pathetically low because of the incidence of diseases, poor knowledge of agronomy and lack of good varieties. At the P.A.U. an intensive research programme for the improvement of pulses is under way. A new variety, Moong G 65 of *Phaseolus aureus* has been evolved through selection. This variety, when sown in the third week of April, after the wheat harvest, ripens in 65 days and is capable of yielding about 12 quintals per hectare on an average. It can be sandwiched commendably between the wheat crop and the main monsoon crops like maize or rice. The seed of this variety is being rapidly multiplied and it is hoped that its cultivation will enable the farmers to have three crops in a year. If this variety succeeds the production of moong pulse will sharply increase.

In addition to Moong G 65 several other varieties of pulses with yield potentials as high as 25 quintals per hectare are being tested.

(e) Other Crops

The P.A.U.'s improvement programme is highly broad-based. Improvement work is in progress on almost all the crops grown in the state, such as cotton, gram, maize, sugarcane, fodders, oilseeds, fruits and vegetables. Almost in every crop new improved varieties have been evolved and released. The benefits that have accrued to the state from these improved varieties are highly encouraging. A list of various crop varieties evolved and released by the P.A.U. ever since its inception is given on next page.

The crop-improvement programme is a continual process. The scientists of the University are constantly striving for further improvements in yield, quality, disease and pest resistance, etc. The future holds out every promise for improved and better crop varieties.

Table 8

S. No.	Name of crop	Margin of superiority to the standard	Year of release
1.	**Bajra**		
	S. 530	5%	1965
	H.B. No. 1	60% to 100%	1966
2.	**Cotton**		
	J. 34 (American cotton)	25%	1966
	G. 27 (indigenous cotton)	25%	1969
3.	**Fodder**		
	N.B. 21	30%	1970
4.	**Maize**		
	Vijay	37%	1969
5.	**Oilseeds**		
	Groundnut C 145	20%	1968
	Castor No. 1	30%	1965
	Yellow Sarson Pb. 24	20%	1966
	B.S.H. No. 1	21% to 37%	1966
	Til Pb. No. 1 (Sesame)	25%	1966
	Linseed Lc 185	26%	1970
6.	**Rice**		
	Norin 18	25%	1967
	IR 8	40%	1968
	Jhona 351	34%	1968
	Jaya	21.8%	1971
7.	**Sugarcane**		
	CO 1148	15%	1967
	CO 67-11	26%	1968
	CO J. 58	36%	1970
	CO 1158	12%	1970
	CO 975	15%	1970
8.	**Wheat**		
	C 306	17%	1965
	PV 18	60% to 90%	1966
	Kalyan-Sona 227	30% to 100%	1967
	S 308	45% to 90%	1968
9.	**Guara**		
	227	43%	1971
10.	**Moong**		
	G 65	51% to 61%	1971
11.	**Soyabean**		
	Bragg	28.7%	1971
12.	**Tobacco**		
	C 302	29%	1965
13.	**Tomato**		
	S 12	70%	1967
14.	**Musk-melon**		
	Hara Madhu	43%	1967

(f) Improved Crop Agronomy

To exploit the maximum genetical yield potential of improved crop varieties, sound agronomic practices need to be evolved. The age-old agronomic practices in the state were meant for varieties with limited yield potentials. For new and highly fertilizer-responsive varieties far-reaching changes in agronomy were called for. If knowledge of suitable agronomic practices for new crop varieties was not rapidly gained, the scope for improvement in production would have been limited.

The research programmes are coordinated by the Directorate of Research which serves all the five constituent colleges. The breeders, agronomists, soil scientists, entomologists and plant pathologists cooperate to work out speedily schedules for agronomy, pest and disease control, etc. for new crop varieties. Such a coordinated approach enables the release of new varieties after thorough testing and after properly ascertaining their agronomic needs. Even after the release a watch is maintained to meet the challenge of changing conditions.

When dwarf wheats were introduced in 1965 the emphasis on the application of nitrogenous fertilizers was concurrently stepped up as these varieties are highly fertilizer-responsive. In the initial years of introduction, the response per kilogram of applied nitrogen in soils with low to medium nitrogen was about 20-35 kilograms of additional grains. The responses from similar quantities of phosphorus were much less and were generally to the extent of three to six kilograms of additional grains per kilogram of P_2O_5 applied. The position has materially changed during the last five years. Now the responses from applied phosphorus are generally equal to and sometimes higher than those from nitrogen. Many farmers who apply only nitrogenous fertilizers and do not pay adequate attention to P and K get reduced yields. These findings are borne out by experiments at the University research stations and in the cultivators' fields.

In a large number of cases, higher yield levels have promoted deficiencies of micronutrients, particularly that of zinc. In soils where zinc or phosphorus is deficient, a good crop of wheat cannot be raised by applying liberal quantities of nitrogen alone. In zinc-deficient soils the addition of zinc sulphate at the rate of 20 to 25 kilograms per hectare to the soil or its spraying at 0.4 per cent to the foliage dramatically improves plant growth and productivity.

The experiments conducted by the scientists of the University have shown that when 60 kilos of P_2O_5 was combined with 120 kilos of nitrogen in soils of low or medium phosphorus status the grain yield increased by 14 and 19 quintals per hectare respectively as compared with that obtained from 120 kilos of nitrogen alone.

With emphasis on intensive cultivation it is becoming imperative that manures and fertilizers are judiciously applied and are based on soil and plant tests. The University provides this service free to the farmers. It has been observed that the farmers who applied nutrients as recommended by the University on the basis of soil analysis data earn Rs 200 to Rs 1,000 per hectare more than those who followed blanket recommendations. The facility is now being increasingly availed of by the farmers and since the inception of the University 0.425 million soil samples have been tested for the farmers.

Pest and Disease Control. Pests and diseases can seriously damage and even completely annihilate crops if adequate preventive and curative measures are not taken in time. This important aspect is being tackled by the University's scientists in two ways. Firstly, efforts are in hand to evolve crop varieties resistant to pests and diseases. Secondly, chemical and other measures for control are being studied. The spray schedules which have been devised for various crop pests have been found very effective and are being widely adopted by the farmers. The six-spray schedule of cotton advocated by the University results in an average yield increase of 560 kilos per hectare; and in oilseeds, where damage from aphids is very severe, even more striking responses have been obtained. It is estimated that if the University's recommendations for controlling various pests are strictly followed, there can be an additional production of the value of Rs 800 million with the current varieties at the existing levels of inputs.

Mechanization. The intensity of cropping in the state has increased from 125 per cent in 1962 to 137 per cent in 1970. There is scope to increase it still further and it is possible to do so if mechanization of agriculture takes place, so that crops are quickly harvested and the land is speedily prepared for the next sowing. The improvement in rural economy is very closely linked with the speed of mechanization. At present, levelling and sowing operations in wheat are mechanized to the extent of 12.9 and 13.1 per cent respectively. Threshing is mechanized up to 98 per cent but harvesting is mechanized only up to 0.18 per cent. In maize, planting is mechanized only up to 2.48 per cent and there is no mechanization at all in harvesting. In potato also the planting and harvesting operations are performed exclusively by manual labour. The slow speed of mechanization is retarding further progress in the state. During 1970 nearly ten per cent of the wheat crop was damaged by early summer rains as it could not be harvested and threshed in time.

For speedy mechanization, there is an urgent need for indigenous low-cost machines capable of efficient operation under local conditions. The University has therefore undertaken a programme for the development and improvement of seed-cum-fertilizer drills, harvesting and threshing-machines and storage appliances. Already, workable prototypes of potato digger-cum-shaker, groundnut-digger and wheat-reaper have been developed and tested. These new machines will not boost agricultural production further but will open new vistas for employment.

Mechanization has so far had the greatest impact on water-lifting and wheat-threshing operations. The number of tube-wells has increased from about 3,500 in 1956 to 180,000 in 1970 and wheat-threshers from under 20,000 in 1964 to 84,000 in 1970. Only six years ago the bulk of the wheat crop was threshed by bullock power whereas during the last harvest 98 per cent was machine-threshed. It may be stated that mechanization has resulted in better wages and greater employment opportunities for agricultural labour—firstly because the machines have by and large replaced animal power, and secondly because the volume of the crops to be handled has tremendously increased. For example, the total production of wheat in 1965-66 was 1.9 million tonnes and the last harvest was 4.8 million tonnes. Handling of the increased production naturally needs more labour and here machines filled the gap.

Future Promise. A few of its contributions mentioned above give an idea of the nature of service that the P.A.U. has rendered to the farming community in the state in a short span of about eight years of its existence. There has been generous support from the farmers, the government and the private agencies. The University's scientists are, however, not complacent. They realize that though a beginning for the uplift of rural Punjab has been made, still they have to go a long way to fulfil the cherished dreams of the founders of this institution.

While considerable progress has been made in the field of crop husbandry, the picture on the animal husbandry side has been rather gloomy, except for the improvement in poultry production. The University is therefore stepping up its animal-improvement programmes.

An ambitious scheme for buffalo improvement through selection, breeding, improved nutrition, etc. has been launched. The research on semen storage, artificial insemination, disease problems of hybrid cattle, and breeding of improved milch goats, etc. has been intensified. New broiler and egg-laying breeds of poultry are being developed.

To provide relief to housewives, the research programmes in the Home Science College are being stepped up with a view to standardizing kitchen equipment and simplifying kitchen procedures to reduce the time spent by the housewife in cooking alone. Emphasis is being increasingly laid on balanced human diet based on available raw materials.

While there is a general sense of satisfaction over the rapid increase of irrigation resources in the state, yet the University's scientists are concerned about the utilization of groundwater both in application of the presently available water and the future exploitation of this precious resource. Research programmes on various systems of irrigation are in hand. Similar programmes on the geology, the geophysical characteristics, and the geohydrology of acquifers are contemplated.

It is intended to encourage the University's graduates to take up the task of rural development and reconstruction as soon as their services in sufficient numbers become available after meeting the existing urgent needs. Such graduates in the fields of agricultural engineering, veterinary medicine, or agriculture will be encouraged to settle in villages and set up centres for providing the know-how and materials for the supply and use of fertilizers; for the supply, use, and repair of farm machinery including that for pest and disease control of crops and animals.

It is hoped that with the programmes already under way and those envisaged the University will be able to speed up the transformation of rural Punjab in the right direction with the desired speed.

Selected farmers come by buses to the campus of the Punjab
Agricultural University to learn new techniques of farming

Farmers making a round of the demonstrations in the Punjab
Agricultural University

Women take avid interest in the educational programme at
the farmers' festival at the Punjab Agricultural University

Farmers watching a demonstration at the P.A.U. Farmers' Fair

There is great demand for literature on crop-growing among the farmers

A farmer learning the use of a wheel-harrow

Mechanic shops provide a new avenue of employment in towns

Farmers buying improved seed at the P.A.U. agricultural fair

he village carpenters who made the traditional agricultural instruments
e now designing and manufacturing power-operated machinery.
Jarnail Singh with his tractor-mounted reaper

tractor is a multi-purpose machine and has been very useful in wheat
threshing

The ancient method of threshing wheat with bullock-drawn *phalas* is now a rare sight in Punjab

Temporary connections for electricity are provided for electric motors to operate wheat threshers

Custom-threshing with tractor-driven threshers is gaining popularity in Punjab. A farmer carries a thresher on a tractor trolly to his farm

Farmers transporting steel pipes for tube-wells are a common sight on Punjab roads

In 1970-71, Punjab contributed two-thirds of the national wheat surplus
The nation's share travels to markets in trucks and trollies

Punjab's numerous grain markets are choked with wheat during the harve
season.   This is a view of Khanna mandi, 48 kilometres from Ludhiana

Taxis have multiplied on rural roads

Villagers show preference for whisky and
beer over the country brew

An educated wife is more useful around a modern farm. Farmers' daughters attend a rural college for girls at Sidhwan village, 24 kilometres from Ludhiana

Link roads have transformed the Punjab countryside, and have helped in the transformation of agriculture

Wheat is harvested in the last week of April, and the entire countryside of Punjab is covered with bundles of harvested wheat

"If you come with me to the fair, I will carry your child," says the husband in a folk song. Now he carries the wife and the child both on his cycle as they go places

Banks have opened branches in villages and provide credit to the farmers

Ploughing to the accompaniment of music from a transistor radio is no longer a dull occupation

Repair shops for tractors have multiplied in the towns of Punjab

There is a general desire for clean clothes among the farmers of Punjab. As such, shops selling cloth are doing flourishing business

Shops selling improved seed and plant-protection chemicals and plant-protection equipment are a new phenomenon in Punjab towns

A tube well brings a better life to a village.

12. Cooperative Credit Societies

Cooperatives have played an important role in the supply of finance, in crop production and in the development of land and water resources. To fit them for this role, structural changes have been made in the cooperative movement, and procedures have been modified to link credit with production on the one hand and with supplies and marketing on the other.

Cooperative Credit. The cooperative movement in India was introduced as a sequel to rural indebtedness and the first legislation was the *Cooperative Credit Societies Act* of 1904 which enabled the organization of credit cooperatives. The cooperative credit society represented an organization with a very selective membership advancing nominal amounts as loans to meet a limited number of contingencies, seldom related to production and with negligible local participation in its resources. The objective of the cooperative movement during that period was not so much to replace the money-lender as to curb his acquisitive propensities and to introduce wholesome practices in the dealings of the private money-lending agencies. Even in achieving this limited objective the performance of the cooperative movement, taking the country as a whole, was not encouraging.

Punjab was one of the few states in which the credit cooperative movement had a good record. The first experiment in co-operation was made in Punjab when a cooperative society was organized in the village of Panjawar in 1895. The purpose of the society was threefold: (*i*) to save common land from erosion through joint action; (*ii*) to make ordinary advances to the members; and (*iii*) to help the members redeem their mortgages.

The society, though unregistered, worked very successfully and was able to save common land from erosion by hill torrents. It also enabled the members to redeem their mortgaged lands.

The development of the movement in Punjab after 1904 was characterized by excellent supervision by the Cooperative Department of the State Government and an equally good participation by the members. Punjab was fortunate in having a line of illustrious Registrars, like H. Calvert, M.L. Darling, and C.F. Strickland, who laid the foundations of a sound cooperative movement. By 1915, the number of societies in the state stood at 3,310, including 38 Central Cooperative Banks, with a working capital of two crore rupees. In 1939, the number of societies stood at 2,434 with a membership of 965,000 and a working capital of Rs 17.14 crores. The number went up to 27,054 in 1946 with a membership of 1,124,000 and a working capital of Rs 24.45 crores. But with all this numerical bounty, the performance was inadequate in respect of coverage of villages and their population.

The assessment of the cooperative movement in qualitative terms in Punjab during the pre-independence period however is that it succeeded though partially in achieving its limited objectives. Partly due to the cooperative movement and partly due to the wartime boom, farmers were able to free themselves at least to some extent from the shackles of the money-lender. The rate of interest on money-lenders' credit came down and malpractices became less common. Though built-in procedural arrangements had not yet been evolved for linking cooperative credit with the production programmes of the farmer, the effort generally was to advance loans for production.

Orientation in Objectives. A real orientation in the objectives of credit cooperatives came about in the post-independence period. The All India Rural Credit Survey Report which can be said to have brought about a radical change in cooperative policy for the first time concluded that the cooperative movement had "failed" in the sense that: (*i*) It had covered only seven per cent of the rural families in the country; (*ii*) it had advanced only 3.1 per cent of the total borrowings of the countryside;

and (*iii*) the loans advanced had hardly any direct link with production.

For the first time the report spelt out the role of the movement in the context of national needs and held that its objectives should be to assess the production needs of the entire farming community; equip itself fully to meet these needs to the full extent; and play a developmental role in transforming the agricultural economy from subsistence level to commercial level.

The objectives of the movement have since been completely changed. The cooperative credit societies of today are mass organizations with a universal coverage of rural families and advancing adequate funds to the farmer for progressively larger investments in their farms, the loans being linked to the maximum extent to the production requirements and as far as possible with advances in kind. The criteria of good credit which the cooperatives are now following are that: (*i*) it must be adequate, i.e. in quantity it must be commensurate with the growing production requirements of the farmer; and (*ii*) it must be suitable, i.e. the loan should be given at a reasonable rate of interest and linked with the production requirements.

Structural Changes. Along with the new orientation in objectives, structural changes of great significance have come about in the post-independence period. The Rural Credit Survey Committee disapproved the idea of continuing with the small-sized Raiffeisen model societies with unlimited liability at the village level. Small societies, owing to their limited business turnover and nominal incomes, could not afford to avail of the services of trained staff. The result was that they could neither gain nor retain the confidence of the depositors and could not equip themselves financially adequately to serve the needs of the members. The so-called advantage of mutual knowledge and collective responsibility was also absent in practice. The Report, therefore, recommended the organization of "large-sized" societies having the special features of large membership, limited liability, trained wholetime staff and a regular office so that they should be able to muster local resources at the same time and to advance production credit to the entire farming community on a larger scale.

When the pattern of large-sized societies was adopted in Punjab, they were established in villages after careful selection. By 1962, 420 large-sized societies had been established in Punjab with a membership of 159,000 and a working capital of Rs 4.31 crores.

An assessment indicates that large-sized societies were ahead of small societies not only in respect of paid-up share capital but also in the volume of deposits and the level of loaning operations, even after making allowances for their larger jurisdiction.

Yet another step in the direction of ensuring viability of local cooperative credit units has been the reorganization of rural credit cooperatives into service cooperatives. These societies were established mostly by making new by-laws for the existing credit societies. The scope of their operations was enlarged and their functions included not only the supply of credit but also the supply of agricultural inputs, agricultural machinery and consumption requirements. In a way these functions were expected to be performed by the existing credit societies also to some extent, but their task was simpler. They confined their activities largely to the grant of loans. Other functions, if at all performed, received secondary attention and seldom were the two—credit and production programmes—linked together. In the service cooperatives the centre of gravity has shifted from the counters of the societies' offices to the cultivators' fields. Increase in production is the core of the task undertaken by them.

The effort which began with the recommendations of the Committee on Cooperative Credit headed by V.L. Mehta resulted in the reorganization of the entire cooperative credit structure at the village level into service cooperatives. After the Hyderabad Conference of State Ministers for Cooperation in June 1964, the effort has been to further reorganize the structure at the village level in accordance with the concept of viability. The criteria of viability are: ability of the society to have a regular office; to appoint wholetime paid staff; to contribute to the reserves on the scales considered necessary and to pay reasonable returns on capital. To meet these criteria, the non-viable societies were either amalgamated into units in the neighbourhood or are being assisted to make them viable.

Simultaneously, the federal structure at the top has been strengthened. In each district there had been a number of central financing agencies including credit unions. During the First Five-Year Plan a programme of amalgamating these units into a strong district cooperative bank was initiated and the number of central financing institutions was reduced from 65 to 18. The share capital of the Central Cooperative Banks was also strengthened by establishing links between shareholders with the loans advanced to the affiliated societies. The present ratio of linking shares with loaning is 1:12. With the increasing turnover of business, the Central Cooperative Banks earned sufficient profits, most of which have during the years been allocated to funds, thus strengthening the owned funds of the institutions.

On the recommendations of the Rural Credit Survey Committee, State Governments also became partners in all the Central Cooperative Banks, the State Governments' contributions to share capital being on a matching basis. The total share capital contribution by the State Government to the 17 Central Cooperative Banks and the State Cooperative Bank in Punjab now stands at Rs 66,651,900. This policy has helped in increasing the borrowing limits of the institutions and in developing public confidence in them. Later, as a result of the recommendations of the Mehta Committee on Cooperative Credit, the State Government also started contributing shares to the selected service cooperatives.

One of the weak points in the functioning of the credit structure has been the societies' inability to attract deposits from the public. A determined effort was therefore made at all levels to increase deposits. The result has been that Punjab is on top so far as deposits in primary societies are concerned. Total deposits in the primary credit societies (service cooperatives) stood at Rs 14.12 crores on 30 June 1969 making an average of Rs 33 per member and Rs 10,500 per society. As a result of reorganization of the central financing structure in the state, the strengthening of its share capital base, etc., it has been possible for them to channel adequate funds to the farmers through their primary service cooperatives.

Procedural Orientation. Though the pioneers of the cooperative

movement in the state have throughout emphasized that cooperative credit institutions should provide only production
finance, in practice most of the loans were being utilized for
non-productive purposes. Moreover, the credit limits were
linked not with the production programme of the farmer
but with his land holdings. A person who was paying more
land revenue could get a larger credit and the one who was
paying less would get proportionately less. This continued even
after independence because no built-in arrangement for linking
credit with the production programme of the farmer could be
evolved. For the first time the Rural Credit Survey Committee
recommended that large-sized societies should advance crop
loans. The system as recommended was based on the following
four considerations:

1. Production should be the main purpose of disbursement
of finance;
2. short-term loans be advanced on the basis that a crop is
expected not primarily that a title exists;
3. loans be limited in amount to the estimated outlay on
raising the crops; and
4. recoveries be made as and when the crops are sold from
the proceeds of the sale.

Crop-Loan System. The crop-loan system introduced into Punjab
in 1967 envisages that the credit needs of cultivators should be
determined with reference to the requirements of production
in respect of different crops to be grown by them in the ensuing
season, individual credit limits being fixed subject to the repaying
capacity. The cultivators' requirements are classified as under:

COMPONENT 'A'   Cash required for undertaking cultivation
with traditional methods, involving a little
or no outlay on fertilizers. This component
is limited to one-third of the value of the
gross produce of the member. It may
include labour charges.

COMPONENT 'B'   Credit required for inputs, i.e. chemical
fertilizers, insecticides and seeds, only to be

given in kind.

COMPONENT 'C'   Additional cash requirements not exceeding 50 per cent of the value of the kind in component 'B' to meet expenditure on account of the application of fertilizers, insecticides, etc.

COMPONENT 'D'   Additional cash amount given as an incentive to a member who sold his produce through the cooperative society during the previous year.

A schedule indicating the average cost of cultivation per acre, crop-wise and component-wise, is obtained from the District Agricultural Officer. The schedule so received is amended to suit the local requirements of each area in a field workers' conference held every year in early October.

The scales of finance fixed for the ensuing year are communicated to the primary service cooperative by 15 October. The supervisory staff of the department/bank assists the primary societies in preparing the normal credit-limit statement in respect of each member. The approval of the managing committee to these limits is then obtained and they are forwarded to the Central Cooperative Banks by 31 January through the Assistant Registrar, Cooperative Societies. The banks then sanction limits for each society by 20 February. The periods of financing have been fixed from 15 February to 30 September for the Kharif crop and 1 October to 14 February, for the Rabi crop. The loans so advanced are recovered up to 30 December for the Kharif crop and 30 June for the Rabi crop.

Progress of Cooperative Credit. Cooperative credit work has been making steady progress in the state and during the last decade there have been spectacular results.

Coverage of Villages and Members
During the Second Five-Year Plan period campaigns were launched to cover every village with a cooperative society and to encourage the representation of every farming household in a village credit cooperative. The result was that in 1963-64, 100

per cent of the villages were covered. Similarly, coverage of
households through membership has been growing quite fast.
By 1961, 79.8 per cent of cultivator-households were covered by
service cooperatives. The percentage rose to 98.2 in 1965-66.
Thus almost all cultivator-households were covered by the
cooperatives as early as 1965-66.

Loaning Operations

Another major indicator of the performance of cooperative credit
societies relates to lending operations. The following table shows
the yearly progress in loaning operations in Punjab with comparative all-India figures alongside.

Table 9
(Rupees in crores)
Statement showing the loans advanced during the year

	1960-61	1963-64	1965-66	1967-68	
Punjab figures	11.76	18.70	27.49	42.81	includes Haryana figures.
All-India figures	202.75	297.14	341.64	404.58	

These figures show that whereas in 1960-61 Punjab had advanced
5.88 per cent of the total loans advanced in India, during 1967-68
the advances in Punjab constituted 10.25 per cent of the all-India
advances, indicating a much faster rate of growth as compared
with the rest of the country. During 1969-70 loaning in Punjab
further increased to Rs 61.63 crores (excluding Haryana).

As envisaged in the system, emphasis is now being laid on
issuing loans in kind as far as possible. During Rabi 1969-70
loans worth Rs 20.88 crores out of total loans of Rs 29.48 crores
were advanced by the cooperatives in kind in the form of fertilizers
and other agricultural inputs.

Recoveries

The crop-loan system envisages that the loans advanced should
be recovered out of the crop in which they were invested. The
recovery is, therefore, not only a sign of good banking but is
also an indicator of proper utilization of loans. If the recovery

is good, it shows that the loans have by and large been utilized for production purposes. In Punjab, overdues in 1966-67 were only 18.1 per cent as compared with the all-India average of 33.05 per cent.

Long-Term Credit. Whereas short-term loans are given for current agricultural operations, long-term investment is essential for developing land. In this respect also Punjab has been a pioneer as the first land mortgage banks were established in this state. The present structure came into being in 1958 when the Punjab State Cooperative Land Mortgage Bank was established. It started functioning through 27 Central Cooperative Banks which were recognized by this bank as its agents to advance long-term loans. The agency system was abolished in 1962 when 14 primary land mortgage banks were organized mostly at district head-quarters. Later these branches were converted into autonomous primary land mortgage banks. In 1970, 33 primary land mortgage banks were functioning in the state. The land mortgage banking system procures funds through a system of issuing debentures on the guarantee of the State Government and the security of mortgage deeds which vest in a trustee appointed by the State Government.

The loans issued by the land mortgage banks in Punjab have also shown a very good rate of growth as is indicated by the figures below. In less than a decade, long-term loans advanced by the land mortgage banks have gone up from Rs 0.31 crore to Rs 15.82 crores showing a rise of more than 50 times. Moreover, 97 per cent of the loans are given for productive purposes which include Rs 8.44 crores for installation of tube-wells, Rs 2.97 crores for purchase of tractors, Rs 0.2152 crore for construction of field channels, and Rs 0.0982 crore for the levelling of land.

The State Land Mortgage Bank has employed agricultural economists to help in formulating and implementing schemes which are financed with the aid of the Agricultural Refinance Corporation. By this time 21 schemes to finance the construction of tube-wells, to line channels and to level land have been sanctioned. The schemes envisage the construction of 30,550 tube-wells at a cost of Rs 26.28 crores. Schemes are financed through the flotation of special development debentures. Up to

30 June 1970 the bank has floated such debentures of the value of Rs 12.45 crores out of which Rs 11.20 crores has been contributed by the A.R.C. and the remaining Rs 1.25 crores by the State Government.

13. The Punjab State Cooperative Supply and Marketing Federation Limited

Supply of Inputs and Marketing of Wheat. Among the factors which have promoted the Green Revolution in Punjab is the arrangement for the supply of fertilizers, agricultural implements and other essential services to the farmers by the Punjab State Cooperative Marketing Federation Limited.

The federation was registered as an apex cooperative marketing society for Punjab in September 1954, with the primary objective of building an integrated structure for remunerative marketing of agricultural produce and for supplying production inputs to the farmers. The start was quite humble. There were only 13 member societies located at the district level and the federation's function was confined to coordinating supplies to them. With the inception of the Second Five-Year Plan, the federation's activities gained momentum. It obtained exclusive distribution rights for insecticides and pesticides from Tata Fison Limited, for the State of Punjab. It was also entrusted with the job of distributing fertilizers as agents of the Punjab Government in the Department of Agriculture. The federation's size grew with the registration of a cooperative marketing society in each regulated market, which was enlisted as its member.

Supply of Fertilizers. In 1960, the distribution of fertilizers was transferred from the Department of Agriculture to the Co-operative Department, which entrusted it to the federation at its exclusive risk and responsibility. This was, therefore, the real start of providing service to the farmers. In 1967, the work was completely left to the federation so that it had to arrange its own financial resources for the purchase of fertilizers. The organizational sales structure set up by the federation for this activity has unique features:

1. There are about 4,000 sales depots spread all over the state and deep into the countryside so that fertilizers and other production requisites are available to the farmers throughout the state within a distance of three to five kilometres.
2. A uniform price is maintained throughout the state including inaccessible and far-flung areas.
3. Cooperative societies purchasing fertilizers for their members are provided with facilities of special trade discount and free transportation.
4. Elaborate stock arrangements are made at the selling points in coordination with the district authorities so that the production plans of farmers may not suffer for want of fertilizers.
5. A link has been established with the credit institutions e.g. the State Cooperative Bank, the Central Cooperative Banks and the service cooperatives to provide to farmers fertilizers on credit.

The table below shows the quantity and value of fertilizers sold from 1960 onwards.

Table 10
Consumption of Chemical Fertilizers

Year	Quantity (tonnes in '00,000)	Value (Rs in crores)
1960-61	0.39	1.17
1961-62	0.69	2.11
1962-63	1.11	3.41
1963-64	1.42	5.68
1964-65	2.28	9.77
1965-66	2.36	9.03
1966-67	2.58	13.95
1967-68	5.16	18.50
1968-69	8.86	35.44
1969-70	9.00	38.00
1970-71	11.30	47.50

The federation is actively associated with other agencies concerned in promoting and propagating the use of chemical fertilizers by organizing eight soil-testing laboratories in the state where the farmers can get their soil and water chemically tested free of charge. On the basis of such chemical analysis the farmers are advised on the correct use of various types of fertilizers, which enables them to obtain the maximum return on their investment and labour.

A large number of farmers do not know the correct proportions in which different types of fertilizers should be mixed. The federation has set up a granulation plant at Ludhiana with a capital outlay of Rs 0.5 crore. This plant has a rated capacity of 45,000 tonnes per year for producing the N.P.K. mixture in granulated form in various gradations suited to the requirements of different soil types in the state.

The federation has taken active part in the establishment of the Indian Farmers' Fertilizer Corporation Limited, a cooperative agency at the national level for the manufacture of fertilizers. Out of the cooperative equity shares of nine crore rupees of this organization, the federation has subscribed shares valued at Rs 2.5 crores. This entitles the federation to claim about one-third of the total production of the factory for Punjab, which means an assured annual supply of about 260,000 tonnes of fertilizers to the state. In addition, commercial contacts have been established with other manufacturers of fertilizers in the country so that the production plans do not suffer for want of fertilizers.

Stocking of fertilizer is so arranged that there may be no shortage at any selling point during the season when fertilizer is required. Since it is not possible to receive supplies exactly when the stocks are required by the farmer, supplies have to be received continually from the factories taking into consideration the requirements which are worked out by the Agriculture Department. During the peak sowing season, stocks are replenished where necessary at short notice. All the marketing societies are connected by telephone with the federation as well as with the cooperative departmental offices so that the adjustment of stocks can be made at short notice.

Keeping in view the past performance and the estimated

requirements of the future, the following targets have been fixed for the remaining years of the Fourth Five-Year Plan.

Table 11

Targets Proposed for the Fourth Five-Year Plan

(Figures in '00,000 tonnes)

Year	Nitrogenous	Phosphatic	Potassic	Total	
1969-70	9 22	3.51	0.39	13.12	Consumption targets
1970-71	9.00	1.94	0.19	11.13	
1971-72	11.30	5.95	1.05	18.30	Plan targets
1972-73	12.35	6.90	1.10	20.35	
1973-74	14.60	7.80	1.35	23.75	

Seed. The federation has also been arranging the supply of good quality and certified seeds to the farmers. Before the lifting of zonal restrictions on the movement of foodgrains, it arranged to import and supply to the farmers sorghum seed at two-thirds the price at which it was available in the local market. It has also been supplying seeds of hybrid bajra and maize.

Diesel Pump-Sets. The federation has made arrangements for procurement of diesel pumping sets for supply to the farmers against *taccavi* loans sanctioned by the State Government and the cooperative credit agencies. The table below shows the number and value of diesel engines supplied to the farmers from 1966 to 1969.

Table 12

Year	Number	Value (Rs in '00,000)
1966-67	2,762	82.55
1967-68	7,414	236.46
1968-69	10,400	3,317.14

This service had a number of advantages. For example, good-quality engines, such as Kirloskar's which were difficult to get in the open market, were made available according to the choice of the farmer at prices lower by Rs 100 to Rs 125 than the company's listed prices. Moreover, it prevented the misuse of loans.

Plant-Protection Equipment, Pesticides and Insecticides. The federation took up the distribution of insecticides and spraying equipment in 1950. This service was intensified as agricultural production in the state stepped up. In 1965 a special promotional cell was created to promote the use of insecticides and pesticides and plant-protection equipment. Arrangements were made to supply such equipment and pesticides through the network of marketing societies. A formulation plant was set up to prepare standard-quality emulsions of Endrin and Malathion for supply to the farmers at far cheaper rates than those demanded by private trade. The following table indicates the value of plant-protection equipment and pesticides supplied by the federation.

Table 13

Year	Plant-protection equipment (Rs in '00,000)	Insecticides and pesticides (Rs in '00,000)
1965-66	4.10	7.66
1966-67	3.27	7.60
1967-68	4.30	(8.61
1968-69	2.28	41.45

Ground-Spraying Unit. A ground-spraying unit comprising 29 minimicron power sprayers has been set up to render spraying service on contract basis at the rate of Rs 16 per acre per spray. About 100 acres of wheat and 804 acres of citrus plants were sprayed during 1968-69. In 1969-70 this squad sprayed 1,350 acres of cotton, 100 acres of maize and 100 acres of wheat.

This unit also undertook the treatment of newly built godowns of the federation against white ants at three rupees per square metre as against five rupees charged by private firms and treated 28,782.5 square metres of floor area at a cost of Rs 86,347.50. Private firms would have charged Rs 143,912.50 for this work. Thus there was a net saving of Rs 57,465 to the federation.

Aerial-Spraying Unit. The federation's scheme for setting up an aerial-spraying unit of five helicopters has been accepted in principle by the Government of India and the federation has been allocated foreign exchange worth Rs 900,000 to purchase two helicopters.

Marketing of Agricultural Produce. With the increase in wheat production its marketing became a problem. Any weakness in the marketing arrangements would have resulted in a fall in prices and consequent frustration to the farmers. The federation entered into active participation with the state procurement machinery so that the entire produce brought by the farmers to the markets was lifted at government procurement prices, and the farmer was immediately paid the full price. The cooperative marketing structure was put into action to make the operation a success. The following table indicates the volume of work done by the federation in this field.

Table 14

Wheat Purchased

Year	Quantity (Qtls. in '00,000)	Value (Rs in crores)
1964-65	5.00	2.68
1965-66	1.20	0.80
1966-67	9.86	7.91
1967-68	65.00	51.40
1968-69	82.00	64.83
1969-70	61.50	50.21

The efficiency with which the federation handled the operations was praised at all levels.

Storage. The village societies as well as the marketing cooperatives stand in need of godowns to stock fertilizers, insecticides, agricultural implements and machinery. Marketing cooperatives also stand in need of godown space to stock agricultural produce purchased by them. Since the beginning of the First Five-Year Plan financial assistance has been provided to the societies for the construction of godowns. Twenty-five per cent of the amount advanced to them has been treated as a subsidy. Recently the Marketing Federation and the Punjab State Cooperative Bank Limited, with the assistance of the Agricultural Refinance

Corporation, have undertaken a comprehensive scheme for the construction of godowns as detailed below:

Table 15
Construction of godowns

Total capacity so far planned in different phases with estimated expenditure	1969-70 Capacity in tonnes	Value (crores)	1968-69 Capacity in tonnes	Value (crores)
PHASE I	156,000	1.872	156,000	1.872
PHASE II	50,000	0.70	—	—
PHASE III	100,000	—	—	—
Total	306,000	2.572	156,000	1.872

The federation has an engineering cell which is entrusted with the responsibility for the construction of godowns.

Processing of Agricultural Produce. The federation has been encouraging the establishment of various processing factories for paddy and groundnut. Seventeen rice-shellers were installed in rice-growing areas of the state. During the year 1968-69, these societies were helped to purchase 35,450 tonnes of paddy at a cost of Rs 1.90 crores.

A giant groundnut oil complex has been set up at Khanna. It consists of an oil mill with a capacity to crush 100 tonnes of groundnut and 75 tonnes of oilcakes per day. A vanaspati mill with a capacity of 50 tonnes per day at a capital outlay of Rs 0.5 crore is being added to the complex. The federation is providing all financial and managerial help to this complex. The quantity and value of groundnut supplied by the federation to oil mills during 1967-68 and 1968-69 are indicated below:

Table 16
Groundnut supplied

Year	Quantity	Value (Rs in '00,000)
1967-68	2,154 tonnes	30.00
1968-69	4,924 tonnes	85.00

A vegetable dehydration plant of 75 tonnes daily capacity is being installed at Jullundur. Machinery has been imported from Bulgaria. The total capital outlay involved on the land, building and machinery is Rs 7,000,000. Plans are also in hand to set up a grape-processing plant at Giddarbaha and insecticide plants at Mohali and Rajpura.

Three cement pipe plants for the production of N.R.C.C. and R.C.C. pipes for underground irrigation have been set up at Moga, Ropar and Sarna with a production capacity of one to two hundred thousand running feet of pipes per annum.

A network of 23 additional processing units comprising cotton-seed, cattle feed, grapevine, and chillies processing etc. is being planned.

14. Agro-Industries in the Private Sector

Punjab's agricultural strategy is built round the need for increased total production as well as higher returns per person engaged in agriculture. This is feasible only if the inputs like power, water, fertilizers and chemicals are provided in sufficient quantities for the large-scale production of high-yielding plant types and for bringing most of the agricultural land under multiple-cropping. Storage of power for performing various agricultural operations and for lifting ground water has already created a bottleneck. It has been recently estimated that approximately 200,000 tractors (mostly in medium and small sizes) would be required by 1980 to maintain the planned rate of agricultural progress in Punjab. This estimate is based on the minimum energy input requirement of 1 h.p. per hectare in 1980 to achieve a production level of three tonnes per hectare. It is also estimated that a very large number of seed-drills, planters and equipment for preparations of seed-bed, plant protection, harvesting, threshing, etc. would be required. The total investment on tractors and farm machinery in Punjab by 1980 may be as high as Rs 500 crores. This, however, would be feasible only if strong industrial support in terms of manufacturing, marketing, and maintenance of the machinery is built up quickly.

Present Status. The present farm machinery industry of the state owes its development substantially to the initiative and hard work of some artisans. Many of these mechanics started their one-room shops in the early part of this century manufacturing items like Persian wheels, steel ploughs and cane-crushers.

Some of them could foresee the agricultural developments in the state and tried to come up with innovations to match the changing requirements of the farmers. Some of these innovations have influenced agricultural mechanization in the whole country. One such example is that of Sunder Singh, who started with Persian wheels in the early part of the century and now owns one of the most reputed thresher-manufacturing units in the country. The machine—the Ludhiana Thresher—developed by him has become popular in all wheat-growing regions of the country and has been responsible for the development of a wide range of threshing equipment and establishment of new farm machinery industry in Punjab and neighbouring states. In Punjab it would not have been possible to handle the wheat harvest during the last few years if the power-threshers were not there.

Many other mechanics have played a pioneering role in the development and manufacture of other implements and machinery like sowing and plant-protection equipment. At present, there are 400 farm machinery manufacturing units in the state, all characterized by small size and limited resources. It is because of the enterprising men who have led these units that the farm machinery industry in the state could continue to exist and even develop. But the limited finances, lack of modern technical know-how and storage of raw materials and power have become serious problems now and the existing farm machinery industry, unless thoroughly reorganized and strengthened, will not be able to meet the needs of future agricultural development.

Reorganization.

Regrouping

The farm machinery manufacturing units are widely scattered. In most cases these units are located on small plots with limited scope for extension. Facilities for proper storage of raw materials are inadequate in general. The practice of purchasing farm machinery directly from the manufacturer will continue in the future. However, owing to unfavourable and scattered locations and limitations of space, the farm machinery industry in the state is not in a position to establish satisfactory showrooms, preferably at one location, which the farmers could conveniently visit for the selection of equipment. The arrangements for storing the manufactured product are also unsatisfactory because of lack of space. As a starting point, the farm machinery manufacturing industry in different towns should be encouraged to regroup at new locations where enough space for future extension of manufacturing activities, showroom facilities and storage may be provided. Allotment of sufficient area for farm machinery manufacture in the future planning of industrial estates is essential.

Specialization

At present, most of the farm machinery manufacturers are trying to handle all manufacturing operations involved in the production of their items of machinery. This is something equivalent to the subsistence farming of the past when the farmer tried to grow a bit of every crop needed for his own consumption. This practice does not permit the use of modern tools and techniques in production. If the farm machinery industry in the state is to survive and grow in future, specialization in production will have to be introduced both for the farm machinery and the ancillary industries. For example, one unit specializing in the manufacture of fluted rolls can supply this component to all manufacturers of seed-drills in the state and even outside at a much lower cost than the manufacturers have to incur now in making their own fluted rolls. At the same time, the quality of the component would be superior because the unit specializing in its manufacture would be able to afford superior tools and techniques in its production.

Quality Control

At present, none of the farm machinery manufacturing units in the state is large enough to maintain a standard quality control organization. With the regrouping of the farm machinery manufacture and its location at one site in a town, it will be feasible to establish and maintain common quality control facilities.

Technical Guidance

Punjab has a large number of unemployed young engineers. The industry, at present manned mostly by mechanics, could benefit greatly from the service of qualified engineers. The reorganization and further development of the farm machinery manufacture in the state will depend considerably on its acceptance of modern engineering know-how and on the employment of trained engineering personnel. At the same time a mechanism should be developed to make the technical guidance of the experienced production engineers and the agricultural engineers available to the industry. The National Productivity Council is already working in this direction. However, these efforts need to be strengthened by organizing strong consultancy and extension education programmes in the agricultural universities oriented towards helping farm machinery manufacturers.

Power

The shortage of power in the state has been felt seriously in all sectors of public and private economy. Unless drastic steps are taken, the shortage of electricity will persist and may even get more acute because of the increasing demand—up to 1978-79. Considering the special importance of the farm machinery industry in the state, priority treatment will have to be given to it in the power programme.

Raw Materials

The shortage and non-availability of the following raw materials is causing serious bottlenecks in the farm machinery industry:

GROUP 1.　　Pig-iron.
　　　　　　　Billets.
　　　　　　　CRCA (Cold-Rolled Closed Annealed) sheets—
　　　　　　　　10 to 12 gauge.
　　　　　　　GP (Galvanized Plain) sheets—16 to 20 gauge.
　　　　　　　MS (Mild Steel) plates—mostly in 6 mm size.
　　　　　　　MS Angles.
　　　　　　　Structurals.

GROUP 2.　　Carbon steels in EN specifications such as:
　　　　　　　　EN 8 shaft steel;
　　　　　　　　EN 15 cold-drawn bright rods;
　　　　　　　　EN 19 A cold-drawn polished round bars;

EN 21 round bars;
EN 42 for discs;
EN 45; and
EN 362 cold-drawn bright round bars.

GROUP 3.   Alloy steels required for:
Tiller blades and rotavator tines;
Soft centre steel for moldboards;
Gudgeon pin steel;
Circlip steel;
Duaflex ring;
Vertical hollow shaft;
Valves (inlet and exhaust valves);
Stampings for electric motors, dynamo grade
steel sheets; and
Steel wire for coupler springs—IS 4454-2 of
1967.

GROUP 4.   Stainless steel sheets—18 and 20 gauge.
Stainless steel shafting.

GROUP 5.   Malleable and Grey Iron castings.

The shortage of MS sheets in all gauges has been extremely
serious recently. The shortage of raw material has resulted in
the use of poor-quality material. It has been reported that the
farmer had to pay nearly Rs 500 extra for a tractor-mounted
seed-drill because of the high prices of steel in the open market.

New Industry. It is estimated that nearly 25,000 tractors are
in use in the state. By 1980, the total number of tractors in use
in the state, provided they are made available to the farmer, as
mentioned earlier, may be about 200,000. Taking into consideration the requirements for new additions and replacements of the
old tractors, a production capacity of 30,000 tractors per year
appears to be reasonable to meet the needs of the state. Nearly
90 per cent of the agricultural holdings being less than 12 hectares
in size, the demand for tractors is likely to be mostly in small
and medium sizes, i.e. from 15 to 30 h.p. At present there is
not even one tractor manufacturing unit in the state although

the Industrial Development Corporation has plans of manufacturing a 20 h.p. machine in the near future.

The agro-industries in the private sector in Punjab have a tremendous potential for development to support the future agricultural strategy of the state. The changed circumstances, however, demand that these industries are extended immediately and generous assistance to reorganize themselves into more modern units to which satisfactory amounts of power and raw materials are made available.

15. Other Factors

Irrigation. Irrigation is the most important ingredient in the package of practices for intensive cultivation. Without assured irrigation, chemical fertilizers, which are a costly input, cannot be used with confidence by the farmers. An important factor which has contributed to the Green Revolution in Punjab is the high percentage of irrigated area, particularly by tube-wells which are owned by the farmers themselves. Thus these farmers have an assured source of irrigation at their command and they have made good use of it in raising the intensity of cultivation. Moreover, the Mexican wheat requires seven to eight irrigations which must be made available at particular stages of plant growth, e.g., tilling, grain formation, and grain filling to get optimum yield.

The total geographical area of Punjab is 5.03 million hectares of which 4.05 million hectares is cropped. Wells, tube-wells and canals are the main sources of irrigation. The total irrigated area is 2.88 million hectares out of which 1.29 million hectares is irrigated by canals and 1.59 million hectares is irrigated by wells and tube-wells. In other words, 44.7 per cent of irrigation is by canals and 55.2 per cent is by wells and tube-wells. Only 0.02 per cent is irrigated by other sources.

In 1966, after the reorganization, Punjab had 1.001 million hectares irrigated by wells and tube-wells. This increased to 1.59 million hectares in 1970-71. By March 1972, Punjab had 232,000 tube-wells and pumping sets and about an equal number of wells.

In joint Punjab, before independence, 5.48 million hectares

were irrigated by canals but the partition of the country left Punjab (India) with only 1.79 million hectares of canal-irrigated land. In 1966, after the reorganization into present Punjab and Haryana, Punjab had 1.28 million hectares of the canal-irrigated land. In 1969-70, canal-irrigated land in Punjab was 1.30 million hectares. The total length of the canals, including all mains, branches and distributaries, is about 21,600 kilometres.

The sources of irrigation vary within the state, corresponding to the variations in topography and the water-table. Near the hills, that is, in Ropar, Hoshiarpur and Gurdaspur, the land surface is comparatively undulating and is highly dissected by seasonal streams and is therefore unsuitable for canal irrigation. A rich underground reservoir and nearness of the water-table have made tube-well and well irrigation more feasible in this area. Hence in these districts canals are not important and 75 to 96 per cent of irrigation is from tube-wells and wells. In the western parts of the state, the land surface is a reliefless plain, most suitable for canal irrigation. Because of the deep water-table and excessive salts in the soil, underground water is not suitable for crops. Consequently in this part of Punjab, especially in Ferozepur and Bhatinda, 75 to 90 per cent of the total irrigation is from canals. In the central districts of the state, stretching from Amritsar in the north to Patiala in the south, tube-wells and canals are both equally important for irrigation.

Though 70 per cent of the net sown area of the state is irrigated, there is wide variation in the intensity from region to region, ranging from less than 25 per cent to more than 90 per cent. In six of the 11 districts of the state more than 70 per cent of the net sown area is under irrigation whereas only in two districts is it less than 30 per cent. Amritsar district has the maximum intensity of 90 per cent and Hoshiarpur has the lowest, 22 per cent of the farm area under irrigation.

Canals. In the wake of partition only three canal systems, i.e. the Upper-Bari Doab, the Sirhind Canal and the Western Jamuna Canal fell to the share of Punjab (India), a mere 20 per cent of the rich inheritance of the joint Punjab irrigation system. In order to meet the great demand for irrigation, steps were taken to increase the discharge of the canals to enhance the water allowance for the areas already under irrigation and also to extend irrigation to new areas.

The discharge of the Upper-Bari Doab Canal which irrigates the fertile lands of Gurdaspur and Amritsar districts was increased in 1954-55 from 9,000 cusecs to 21,000 cusecs. The irrigation from this canal which covered an area of 340,000 hectares in 1960-61 was extended to 510,000 hectares in 1967-70. The discharge of the Sirhind Canal was increased in 1954 from 9,000 to 12,500 cusecs. The Ropar headworks were remodelled to provide irrigation to new areas and to increase the water allowance of the existing areas. The Sirhind Canal system irrigates 531,514 hectares of land in the Malwa tract.

Besides improving the old canal systems, construction of new canals was also taken up. A new headworks at Harike, below the confluence of the Sutlej and Beas rivers, was constructed in 1952-53. Total area irrigated from the canals taken from the Harike headworks is 500,000 hectares in the districts of Ferozepur and Bhatinda.

The construction of the Bhakra Canal system is the biggest landmark in canal-irrigation development in Punjab after independence. Apart from remodelling the Sirhind Canal, the Bhakra Canal system includes the construction of the Bhakra Canal and the Bist-Doab Canal. The Bhakra Canal system completed in 1954 utilizes an 18,000 cusecs discharge. The length of the main canal and the branches is about 1,100 kilometres and that of the distributaries about 3,400 kilometres. The total benefited area by this canal is 1.46 million hectares. After the reorganization of Punjab in 1966, 0.68 million hectares of area irrigated by the Bhakra Canal has gone to Haryana. The other canal of the Bhakra complex is the Bist-Doab Canal which takes off from the right end of the Ropar barrage. The canal has an authorized full supply discharge of 1,601 cusecs and provides non-perennial irrigation to an area of 257,000 hectares in Hoshiarpur, Jullundur and Kapurthala districts.

In order to meet the staggering demand for water for irrigation, the work for harnessing two rivers—the Beas and the Ravi—is in progress. Water to the extent of 7.257 million acre-feet will be available from the Ravi-Beas complex. Additional irrigation from the Beas-Sutlej link project when completed will be to 526,000 hectares, and from the Beas Dam to 3.2 million hectares. Whether any share of this irrigation goes to other states is a matter under dispute.

Wells and Tube-wells. The Indo-Gangetic Plain of which Punjab is the westernmost part is blessed with deep alluvium. There is hardly any other tract in the world with such a vast expanse of ground water. Punjab has a number of snow-fed rivers, the Ravi, Beas and Sutlej, flowing through it. A sub-alluvium charged with the perennial rivers exists under the Doabs, and in some places is 4,500 metres deep. This is a unique underground water resource, and nowhere else in the world does such a great storage of underground water exist.

In the present Punjab, the number of wells used for irrigation is fairly high. In spite of canal irrigation, wells have not lost their popularity. Notwithstanding the introduction of the Bist-Doab Canal in 1955 for irrigating land in the districts of Hoshiarpur and Jullundur, the well irrigation in these districts, which is the highest in the whole of the state, has not declined. The total number of wells in the state is about 200,000.

With the development of science and technology newer and more efficient methods were employed for lifting water from the underground. Mechanically or electrically operated tube-wells replaced the old method of withdrawing water by Persian wheels.

Tube-wells are bored for withdrawing underground water for drinking, irrigation and industrial use. A tube-well gives much more water as compared with an open well. The advantage of a tube-well over canal supply is in the fact that the source of water is owned by the individual farmer himself and irrigation is secure. The water courses are short, percolation losses are small and no extensive system of water distribution is required.

Tube-wells were first installed in Punjab in 1908. A set of 16 deep tube-wells was installed near Amritsar to replace irrigation from the Nathuwala distributary which passed through the populated parts of the city. Later, tube-wells were installed in the waterlogged area close to the Upper Chenab Canal, Lower Jhelum and Lower Chenab Canal, and water was pumped back into the canals. At about the same time tube-wells were installed in U.P. in the Gangetic Plain. Field tests show that on an average, tube-wells taken 76 to 91 metres deep into the underground, with a suitable 30-metre aquifer gave a discharge of about 1.5 cusecs. Further, if the tube-wells are spaced three kilometres apart, no interference occurs in their output.

The tube-wells constructed by the State Department were of two types—strainer type and gravel-packed. The gravel-packed tube-wells have an advantage over the strainer type in a larger discharge and longer life.

Besides the small number of state-owned tube-wells, a large number of private tube-wells have been constructed by the land owners since 1950. Impetus to this was provided by Dr M.S. Randhawa, who prepared schemes for rehabilitation of refugee farmers who were allotted evacuee lands. The capacity of a private tube-well is small varying from 0.25 to 0.5 cusec. These tube-wells are shallow—24 to 30 metres in depth and ten centimetres in diameter. In the plains of Punjab where the sub-strata are stratified, cavity type tube-wells are also installed. No strainer is used and in the sub-strata at the bottom of the hard clay the end of the pipe is left open. A cavity is formed there and the tube-well draws water from it. While there are about 1,000 tube-wells constructed by the State Government, there are more than 200,000 (1971-72) private owned tube-wells in Punjab. The number of tube-wells from 1966 to 1972 is given in the table below:

Table 17
Private tube-wells

Year	Number of tube-wells
1968-69	112,280
1969-70	152,380
1970-71	192,280
1971-72	232,280

The Project Circle of the Irrigation Department, Punjab, is investigating the possibility of providing tube-wells capable of giving 1.5 cusecs discharge for compact blocks of 400 acres in different tracts of the state. Based on the success of the trial bores in Hoshiarpur, Gurdaspur, Kapurthala and other districts, production tube-wells are being installed in large numbers.

The cultivators themselves are very enthusiastic over installing shallow tube-wells. Cultivators owning ten acres or more of land have installed tube-wells powered by diesel engines even though diesel is more costly than electric power. A 0.5 cusec tube-well can be installed at a cost of about Rs 5,000.

The surface water resources of Punjab State have already been fully exploited. The additional water required will have to be obtained from underground water resources. A conjunctive use of surface and ground water shall have to be made. Although ground water resources are plenty it is still essential that these should be used judiciously. A scientific study has to be made regarding the existence of aquifers and storage and the movement of water in the aquifers. Excessive overdraft must be avoided to prevent the depletion of ground water. It is necessary that recharge into and discharge from the aquifer should be balanced over a long period.

For conjunctive use of surface and ground water and for a judicious exploitation of the ground water resources, geological, hydrological and geo-hydrological studies of the tract should be made.

16 Manures and Fertilizers

Early in the history of agriculture, man learnt the use of cattle dung and farm wastes to increase the production of crops. Mention of these practices in the Vedic era in our country and in early Greek and Roman literature is a testimony of the awareness of their utility. Until 1840, when Liebig prepared his "Patent Manure," the use of farmyard manure held sway and it is only during the last 130 years that fertilizers have gradually made their impact felt.

Farmyard Manure and Composts. Farmyard manure is a complete manure. Table 18 gives an idea of the average nutrient content of different manures and crop residues. The composition of farmyard manure varies from place to place depending upon the kind of animals, their age, and conditions, food consumed, litter used and the handling and storage which the manure receives before it is spread on the land. On an average, it contains 0.5 per cent nitrogen, 0.25 per cent phosphorus (P_2O_5) and 0.5 per cent potassium (K_2O). In addition, it contains many other secondary and micronutrient elements. Not only does farmyard manure supply the soil with much needed nutrients, it also improves the physical condition of the very light or very heavy or deteriorated soils. It is, however, a low analysis manure and has to be applied in very large quantities to provide the required nutrients. There is a physical limitation as well on its use owing to its inelastic supply.

The actual use of farmyard manure (including compost) in Punjab during 1967-68 was 5.8 million tonnes and is not expected

Table 18
Average nutrient content of manures and crop residues

| Manure/Crop Residue | Content of the nutrient (percentage) | | |
	N	P_2O_5	K_2O
1. Dung, Cattle, Fresh	0.3-0.4	0.1-0.2	0.1-0.3
2. Night Soil, Fresh	1.0-1.6	0.8-1.2	0.2-0.6
3. Poultry Manure, Fresh	1.0-1.8	1.4-1.8	0.8-0.9
4. Urine Cattle	0.9-1.2	tr.	0.5-1.0
5. Ash-household	0.5-1.9	1.6-4.2	2.3-12.0
6. Compost rural dry	0.5-1.0	0.4-0.8	0.8-1.2

Source : *Handbook of Agriculture*, I.C.A.R., New Delhi (1967).

to increase substantially. On the basis of application of 20.3 tonnes of F.Y.M. per hectare, its supplies will meet the requirement of only 0.28 million hectares, which forms about seven per cent of the net cropped area of the state. Table 19 summarizes the position on availability of F.Y.M. and composts in different districts of the state. The figures show that Jullundur district consumes the highest quantity of farmyard manure and compost. Yet, even there it meets only about 14 per cent of the total soil needs. In the district of Bhatinda where consumption of farmyard manure and compost is the least, the gap is much wider.

Table 19
District-wise use of manures in Punjab during 1967-68

| District | F.Y.M. and compost (Kg. per hectare) | |
	On the basis of total cropped area	On the basis of not cropped area
1. Amritsar	520	822
2. Bhatinda	697	815
3. Ferozepur	702	910
4. Ludhiana	724	1,022
5. Patiala	775	1,097
6. Sangrur	826	1,070
7. Kapurthala	1,495	1,826
8. Gurdaspur	1,639	2,285
9. Hoshiarpur	1,713	2,432
10. Ropar	1,837	2,244
11. Jullundur	2,170	2,887

Source : Department of Agriculture, Punjab.

Green Manures. When plants are ploughed under the soil while they are still succulent, they are termed "green manures." There are certain leguminous plants, fodders and fibres whose roots get infected by nodule organisms that have the capacity to fix atmospheric nitrogen. Their inclusion in the cultivators' cropping practice has, therefore, been recommended to restore the depleted soil fertility. The recommendation has, however, been often pushed to the extreme, ignoring the fact that economic factors govern, in the ultimate analysis, the adoption of a practice by the cultivators. Data in Table 20 show that comparable high yields can be obtained by the use of modest amounts of fertilizers. Also, green manure often competes for water with growing crops such as sugarcane and cotton in extreme water scarcity periods. This may well explain why, despite continual efforts by the State Development Department, green manuring did not make much headway. A rational recommendation on the practice of organic manures is that they may be applied to either very light, very heavy or deteriorated saline-alkali soils as a corrective measure. On other arable soils, they may be applied once in a few years, depending upon the resource availability of the farmer. The bulk of the nutrient needs of the crops may be met by the use of chemical fertilizers.

Table 20

Effect of green manures and fertilizers on yield of wheat (C 591) (quintals per hectare) at Nasirpur (Patiala)

Level of nitrogen applied to wheat	Fallow	Guara (green manured)	Guara fodder
Control	30.5	28.9	21.1
15 lbs. N/acre	32.5	32.1	27.4
30 lbs. N/acre	34.9	33.6	30.5

Source : *J. Res.* Vol. III No. 4, 1966.

Fertilizers. There is a large number of different materials which supply nitrogen, phosphorus or potassium to plants but economic considerations and other factors have narrowed the list so that most of the commercial fertilizers in the world are available in the form of a few materials, as shown in Table 21.

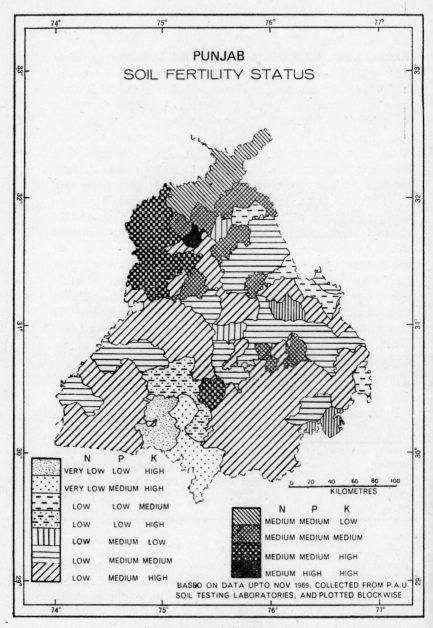

Fig. 8   Punjab soil fertility status.

Table 21
Nutrient content of principal fertilizers

Nitrogen fertilizers

Material	Approximate nitrogen (percentage)
Ammonium sulphate	21
Ammonium nitrate	33
Sodium nitrate	16
Cal-nitre	20-25
Urea	42-45

Phosphate fertilizers

Material	Approximate P_2O_5 (percentage)
Single superphosphate	16
Concentrated superphosphate	32-48
Basic slag	15-25
Rock phosphate	25-30

Potash fertilizers

Material	Approximate K_2O (percentage)
Potassium sulphate	48-50
Muriate of potash	48-60

The agricultural value of a fertilizer is not a constant but depends upon the soil and the crop. The different nitrogenous fertilizers differ from each other in their residual acidity or basicity. For example, ammonium sulphate has a residual acidity equivalent of 107 kilos of $CaCO_3$ per 20 kilos of N supplied by the fertilizer, and sodium nitrate has a residual basicity equivalent of 36 kilos of $CaCO_3$. On this basis, ammonium sulphate is to be preferred over sodium nitrate on alkaline soils. Nitrate nitrogen is readily available for plant use but is also susceptible to leaching losses. The losses are large in light, sandy soils of poor structure. Ammoniacal nitrogen can be adsorbed on surfaces of soil colloidal particles and is thus prevented from leaching at least temporarily. Also, paddy is known to prefer ammoniacal nitrogen. Ammonium nitrate supplies 50 per cent nitrogen in the ammoniacal form and 50 per cent as nitrate, but it is deliquescent and explosive. Upon addition of calcium carbonate, it is converted into calcium ammonium nitrate (Cal-nitre) when it becomes convenient to handle. Urea is a relatively cheap source of nitrogen than ammonium sulphate or calcium ammonium nitrate. When properly applied, it gives comparable yield responses. Until it is hydrolyzed by urease enzymes in the soil, it is not adsorbed on the soil particles and moves readily with percolating water. Therefore urea application should not be immediately followed by an irrigation; urea is also amenable to foliar spray, particularly on orchard crops.

Various phosphatic fertilizers differ chiefly in their solubility. Single superphosphate, which is usually obtained by treating rock phosphate with sulphuric acid, carries water-soluble phosphorus. Its other constituent is gypsum which is removed during manufacture of concentrated phosphates. Basic slag is obtained as a by-product of the steel industry by reaction with the molten iron with calcium carbonate to shed off the phosphorus impurity. The phosphorus in basic slag is citric acid-soluble. Rock phosphate has mineral acid-soluble phosphorus. Because of this difference in phosphorus solubility, single and concentrated superphosphate (triple) are suitable for alkaline and neutral soils of Punjab. Basic slags and rock phosphates are good sources of fertilizer phosphorus in acid soils of adjoining states of Himachal Pradesh and Jammu & Kashmir.

Unlike nitrogen, fertilizer phosphorus moves negligibly in the soil, but it has a strong tendency to react with calcium, iron and aluminium in the soil and become largely unavailable to plants (fixed). It is, therefore, desirable to apply water-soluble phosphates at a depth where the plant roots can readily tap it and in a concentration that sufficient phosphorus will remain unreacted. Drilling below seed or band placement of phosphatic fertilizers to row crops is generally recommended.

Potassium sulphate and muriate of potash are both water-soluble and equally efficient sources of potassium. Nevertheless, large applications of potassium chloride are known to lower the quality of tobacco and potato. Potassium is as soluble and susceptible to leaching as nitrogen, but because it can be adsorbed on the surface of soil colloidal particles, it suffers less leaching than nitrate nitrogen. When more potassium is available in the soil, crops take more of it. Owing to its susceptibility to leaching and luxury consumption, it is advisable to apply small quantities of fertilizer potassium at a time.

Compound Fertilizers. While fertilizers like superphosphate and muriate of potash supply only one nutrient element—nitrogen or phosphorus or potassium—there are others like ammonium phosphate, potassium nitrate and potassium phosphate, which provide two of the three fertilizer elements. The former group of fertilizers is known as straight fertilizers and the latter compound fertilizers. The compound fertilizers which supply phosphorus and potassium are very costly yet, and potassium nitrate is explosive. Therefore the compound fertilizers in use are only those which supply nitrogen and phosphorus. These have several advantages. Firstly, they contain both nitrogen and phosphorus in concentrated form, approaching 64 per cent as in diammonium phosphate. Secondly, assimilation of fertilizer phosphorus often increases due to the presence of ammoniacal nitrogen and *vice versa*. They also cost less to produce, store, transport, handle and apply. Most ammonium phosphates are stable, of crystalline or granular form and hence convenient to handle.

Three types of nitrogen-phosphorus compound fertilizers are in use. Phosphorus in ammonium phosphates is entirely water-soluble. A high citrate solubility is an essential feature of both ammoniated phosphates and nitrophosphates. Because of this difference in water-solubility, the latter group of compound fertilizers is 20 to 25 per cent less efficient in calcareous and alkaline soils of Punjab.

Mixed Fertilizers. When more than one nutrient element is lacking in the soil and mixing of fertilizers is accomplished at a reasonable cost, use of fertilizer mixtures is advantageous. It eliminates gross errors in fertilizer applications, ensures balanced manuring and reduces labour costs. Fertilizer mixtures have a generally good physical condition and store better. Conditioners like bonemeal and oilcakes and secondary and minor elements can also be added with good results. Home mixing of the fertilizers can also be done. The following general rules should, however, be observed for mixing straight fertilizers.

1. Fertilizers containing ammoniacal compounds should not be mixed with basically reactive fertilizers, e.g. lime, basic

slag, or rock phosphate, as losses of nitrogen may occur through the escape of gaseous nitrogen.

2. Water-soluble phosphate fertilizers, for example super-phosphate, triple superphosphate and ammonium phosphate should not be mixed with those containing free lime to avoid reversion.

3. Easily soluble and hygroscopic fertilizers like nitrates, urea and potash salts tend to cake or form lumps after mixing. These should be mixed shortly before use.

4. The slightly acid superphosphate may liberate acids from certain fertilizers like nitrates and chlorides, thus causing material damage. Mixing should, therefore, be avoided.

To meet the nutrient needs of different soils adequately, the following grades of mixed fertilizers are recommended:

Table 22

N		P_2O_5		K_2O	
1	:	1	:	1	General purpose
2	:	2	:	1	For soils high in available potassium
1	:	1	:	0	For soils very high in available potassium
2	:	1	:	1	For soils high in both available phosphorus and potassium
1	:	2	:	1	For soils very low in available phosphorus only
1	:	3	:	0	For leguminous crops
1	:	3	:	1	For leguminous crops

Use of the above grades of fertilizer mixtures at sowing will generally require top dressing of nitrogenous fertilizers later during the crop growth.

When a soil is deficient in only one nutrient or when fertilizer mixing considerably adds to the bill, it is preferable to purchase separate materials and apply them to the soil.

Secondary and Micronutrients. The introduction of high-yielding varieties, necessitating a heavy drain of nutrients, both macro and micro, from the soils, and the growing tendency to use high analysis NPK fertilizers, is making the use of secondary and micronutrients increasingly important for some crops and soils.

As crop yields continue to soar with more adequate fertilization with primary nutrients (nitrogen, phosphorus and potassium), the need for one or more of these micronutrients often becomes limiting. Needs for certain nutrients are becoming too large to be supplied through unpurified raw materials.

Beneficial effects of sulphur application have been observed on groundnut in Ludhiana district. Each year during the last three years, more cases of economically significant responses to added zinc have come to notice, often with wheat which is not a crop particularly susceptible to zinc deficiency. Since the indiscriminate use of micronutrients may cause adverse and toxic effects on crop growth and yield, a correct diagnosis of the deficiency is necessary. In case of micronutrients, therefore, the level of a particular element in balance with the others is much more important. The job of determining micronutrient deficiencies is, however, a formidable one and needs sophisticated equipment for soil and plant analysis.

The principal sources of sulphur are gypsum and superphosphate or ammonium sulphate. In the latter two fertilizers, sulphur occurs as an impurity. The common sources of micronutrients are sulphate salts of metallic elements, borax (sodium tetraborate decahydrate) and sodium molybdate. The amounts of micronutrients supplied in actual practice are quite variable, depending upon soil conditions and the crop to be fertilized.

Table 23

Micronutrient	Pounds of micronutrient element B, Cu, Fe, Mn, Mo, Zn applied per acre
Boron	0.1—1
Copper	5—20
Iron	3—10
Manganese	5—20
Molybdenum	(1/8 to 1 oz)
Zinc	5—10

Commonly, the micronutrients are applied directly to the soil or are used in foliar sprays. In the first case they can be mixed with dry earth collected from the field itself and then broadcast to ensure uniform coverage. The experimental work does not show any particular advantage of foliar spraying.

Micronutrients can be combined with fertilizers during manufacture but the practice runs the risk of chemical reactions leading to the formation of new compounds of reduced availability.

Fertilizer Use in India and Foreign Countries. In order to meet the growing nutrient requirements of soils because of increasing adoption of intensive farming practices, the need to step up fertilizer production in India is quite obvious. The fact that nearly one-third of the increase in foodgrain production in the fourth plan period is expected to result from the application of fertilizers further emphasizes the need to augment fertilizer production. In agriculturally advanced countries of the world, fertilizer consumption has played a singular role in boosting up agricultural production. Table 24 provides a relative comparison of the fertilizer use in India and abroad.

Table 24
Consumption of fertilizers in different countries

Fertilizer consumption per hectare of arable land—1967-68 (kg.)				
Name of country	N	P_2O_5	K_2O	Total
Netherlands	372.6	114.6	139.0	626.2
Japan	153.1	108.0	110.2	371.3
U.K.	122.5	61.8	67.5	251.8
U.A.R.	78.5	17.1	0.2	95.8
U.S.A.	33.8	22.4	19.5	75.7
India	7.0	2.7	1.3	11.0

Source : *Production Year Book 1968*, Vol. 22, F.A.O.

Undoubtedly, we are at the bottom of the list, which stresses the need to increase fertilizer consumption in the country a great deal. The total fertilizer requirements for the country, up to the end of the fourth plan, work out to 3.7 million tonnes N and 2.37 million tonnes of P_2O_5 at the rate of an average plant food supply of 40 kilos per hectare. The inability to produce the desired levels of fertilizer requirements in this country is largely because of late development of fertilizer use and demand for it. Although a number of field experiments had clearly brought out that

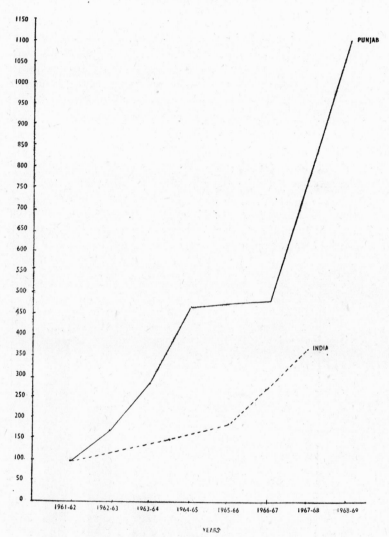

Fig. 9 Trend in fertilizer consumption in Punjab and India 1961-62 to 1968-69.

fertilizers could give large and handsome increases in crop yields, the emphasis continued to be placed on the use of organic manures. The complacency on the part of the administrative and technical personnel, their misplaced emphasis on the virtues

of manures to the exclusion of fertilizers, and lack of adequate
information on the fertilizer needs of different soils together cost
the country valuable time when it should have marched ahead
on a vigorous programme of installing more fertilizer factories.
Now, when the awareness is there and the demand has increased, the prospects of the country having the needed quantities
of fertilizers do not seem to be very bright in the very near
future.   While local manufacture accounts for half of the present
fertilizer used, the other half has got to be imported.   The
demand is now more than four times the availability and it is on
the increase.

State-wise Comparison. A comparison of fertilizer use in different
states of India for the year 1968-69 (Table 25 and Figs. 9 and 10)
indicates that Punjab consumes the largest amount of plant

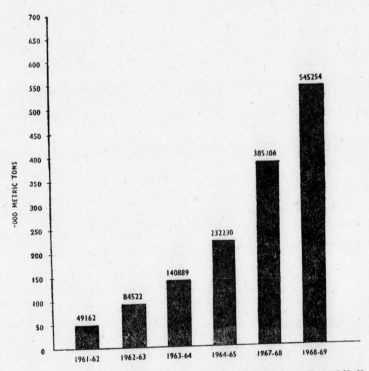

Fig. 10   Consumption of chemical fertilizer in Punjab 1961-62 to 1968-69.

food nutrients per unit of cropped area, followed by Delhi, Kerala and Tamil Nadu. The situation has improved only during the last two years, when the consumption increased from 10.05 kilos of plant food per hectare in 1966-67 to 29 kilos in 1968-69. However, there is no room for complacency. Even this figure is far below the crop/soil needs of our state and the quantity used in several agriculturally advanced European countries.

Table 25
Plant food consumption in major states of India (1968-69)

	State	N	P_2O_5	K_2O	Total
		(kg/ha agricultural land)			
1.	Andhra Pradesh	7.56	2.27	0.34	10.17
2.	Assam	1.79	0.45	0.41	2.65
3.	Bihar	3.39	0.25	0.31	3.95
4.	Gujarat	4.91	2.99	0.31	8.21
5.	Haryana	9.27	0.35	0.66	10.28
6.	Himachal Pradesh	1.39	0.47	—	1.86
7.	Jammu & Kashmir	1.38	0.14	—	1.52
8.	Kerala	11.33	2.82	8.76	22.91
9.	Madhya Pradesh	1.47	0.56	0.15	2.18
10.	Maharashtra	6.41	1.93	1.09	9.43
11.	Mysore	8.22	1.59	1.00	10.81
12.	Orissa	1.14	0.11	0.09	1.34
13.	Punjab	24.84	3.39	0.77	29.00
14.	Rajasthan	1.46	0.06	0.08	1.60
15.	Tamil Nadu	12.45	2.43	3.13	18.01
16.	Uttar Pradesh	12.16	2.35	1.69	16.20
17.	West Bengal	6.03	1.47	1.40	8.90
	India	7.00	1.69	0.94	9.63

Note : Agricultural land includes total cropped area, permanent pastures, other grazing lands and land under miscellaneous tree crops and groves.

District-wise Consumption and Needs. The fertility status of Punjab soils is shown in Fig. 8. The nitrogen deficiency is fairly general. Approximately 80 per cent of the soils tested in various soil testing laboratories are low or very low in organic carbon and the rest, 20 per cent, are medium. In respect of phosphorus, about 16 per cent soils are low in available phosphorus and the rest predominantly medium. About 33 per cent of our soils are deficient in potassium.

Cropping patterns play an important role in determining fertilizer needs of an area. These vary from one place to another. In general wheat, maize and paddy are the important cereal crops of the state and cover more than 50 per cent of the total cropped area. Bajra is grown largely in Bhatinda and Sangrur districts and accounts for about 3.8 per cent of the total cropped area of the state. Gram is the most important pulse crop, occupying 9.7 per cent of the total cropped area and 25 per cent of the cropped area in Bhatinda district. Groundnut, cotton and sugarcane are the important cash crops and the three crops occupy 4.1, 7.7 and 2.5 per cent of the cropped area in the districts of Ludhiana, Ferozepur and Ropar respectively. Based on the differences in nutrient status of the soils, cropping patterns and package of fertilizer recommendations, the fertilizer needs have been worked out district-wise and are shown in Table 27.

Apparently, Bhatinda district used the least amount of fertilizer (14.9 kilos of plant food per hectare) against the highest fertilizer consumption in Ludhiana district (54.3 kilos of plant food per hectare) in the year 1969-70. The districts of Ludhiana and Jullundur compare favourably in the matter of fertilizer use with some of the agriculturally advanced countries of the world. However, even in these districts fertilizer use falls far short of the actual soil needs. Table 28 summarizes the information on present fertilizer use, 1971-72 targets, and crop needs on the basis of present land use. The figure for consumption of nitrogenous fertilizer in 1969-70 is approximately 50 per cent of the 1971-72 target which itself is about half of the estimated crop needs. Keeping in view the present cropping intensity of 136 per cent and the very real possibility of its rise to 175-200 per cent during the next decade, the estimated fertilizer needs should undergo an upward revision of 33 to 50 per cent.

Distribution of Fertilizers. In the Punjab State, the consumption of fertilizers in 1969-70 shot up to 856,000 tonnes as compared to 5,080 tonnes in 1950-51. Some recent years' figures are detailed in Table 26.

This fast expansion of fertilizer consumption in the state necessitated the setting up of a large number of distributing centres. In Punjab, at present (1968) the total number of distribution

Table 26

Year	Punjab ('000 tonnes)
1966-67	240
1967-68	289
1968-69	553
1969-70	856

Source : Department of Agriculture, Punjab.

Table 27

Consumption and crop needs of plant food nutrients in Punjab
(kg. per hectare)

District	Fertilizer consumption (1969-70)			Fertilizer needs		
	N	P_2O_5	K_2O	N	P_2O_5	K_2O
Amritsar	36.7	4.7	2.2	83.2	36.2	16.8
Bhatinda	14.0	0.8	0.1	95.6	26.4	11.2
Ferozepur	20.1	2.1	0.5	90.8	25.1	12.0
Gurdaspur	27.9	2.9	1.2	87.4	37.0	18.0
Hoshiarpur	22.2	2.7	1.0	100.6	39.7	16.8
Jullundur	37.5	6.3	1.8	109.6	41.6	19.8
Kapurthala	27.6	4.5	2.3	84.2	35.7	16.8
Ludhiana	39.0	13.8	1.5	104.0	39.0	17.4
Patiala	27.0	4.6	0.0	92.8	33.1	15.6
Ropar	19.8	3.1	0.9	94.2	39.8	17.4
Sangrur	22.0	2.5	0.6	98.6	33.1	15.0

Fertilizer needs are based on the present cropping pattern and cropping intensity and package of fertilizer recommendations.

Table 28

Actual consumption, targets and needs of fertilizers in Punjab

	Nitrogen N	Phosphorus P_2O_5 ('000 tonnes)	Potassium K_2O
Total consumption (1969-70)	143.7	28.5	9
Targeted consumption (1971-72)	229.6	120.9	64
Actual crop needs on the basis of soil test and present land use	495.8	218.4	77.2

depots is 5,300. The district-wise figures of centres, along with the total cropped area, are detailed in Table 29.

Table 29

District	No. of distribution centres 1967-68	Total cropped area ('000 hectares) 1967-68
Amritsar	625	542
Ferozepur	625	1,106
Hoshiarpur	500	326
Ludhiana	650	447
Patiala	350	502
Bhatinda	550	827
Sangrur	500	627
Kapurthala	250	159
Ropar	300	183
Gurdaspur	400	345
Jullundur	550	377
Total	**5,300**	**5,441**

Source : *Statistical Abstract of Punjab*, 1968.

The largest cropped area is in the districts of Ferozepur, Bhatinda and Sangrur but the largest number of distributing centres is in Ludhiana. Normally a distribution centre in the state serves the needs within an eight kilometre radius. In I.A.D.P., Ludhiana district, almost every village has a cooperative society depot and only in a few cases have two or more villages been grouped together. With the present level of fertilizer requirements this arrangement has worked fairly well, but with increasing demand distribution centres in the state will have to be increased in number.

With increasing irrigation facilities and wider adoption of new high-yielding varieties, targets of fertilizer consumption in the state have now been fixed at higher levels, as in Table 30.

Table 30

Year	Target ('00,000 tonnes)
1970-71	17.2
1971-72	18.59
1972-73	20.67
1973-74	24.13

Source : Department of Agriculture, Punjab.

The quantity of the fertilizers to be handled would thus increase by nearly three times by 1973-74. This will inevitably require more facilities and arrangements for handling and distribution. The targets can be better achieved if more distribution centres are opened in remote areas in the countryside. In fact, every village should have a fertilizer store. This would mean doubling the number of distribution centres.

Storage of Fertilizers. Fertilizer use by the peasantry is largely seasonal. However, production in the factory is a continual process. In order to make available various fertilizers to the farmers at the proper time it is essential to develop a decentralized storage pattern. In Punjab, the storage capacity available with the cooperatives is 487,000 tonnes of which 264,000 tonnes is in villages and 223,000 tonnes at the railheads. This storage capacity is utilized not only for storing fertilizers but also for sugar, seeds, insecticides and other inputs. With about 863,600 tonnes of fertilizers handled at present, the total storage capacity is barely sufficient even for fertilizers. Many village societies are unable to stock fertilizers according to the farmers' needs. With the prospect that 2,413,000 tonnes of fertilizers will have to be handled by the end of 1973-74, storage facilities need to be expanded fast.

In view of the possibility that the volume of fertilizers to be handled in the near future will be more than 300 per cent of the present use, and the existing storage capacity and distributing centres being inadequate even for present requirements, the cooperatives should open distribution centres with every society (even credit societies) in the villages.

Other drawbacks in handling and distribution of fertilizers are:

1. The railheads have very few covered sheds. As a result, some fertilizers get spoiled during the rains.
2. Generally fertilizer bags are delivered to the farmers without weighing. This sometimes leads to the malpractice of under-weighing. Very often the bags get damaged. This leads to leakage of the fertilizer *en route* and in storage with the farmers.

3. There is considerable transhipment of fertilizers from one district to another which involves extra transportation and handling costs and also delays the supplies at certain places. The distribution needs to be rationally planned for different regions and districts of the state, depending upon their actual and potential demand.

4. Sometimes, because of a shortage of required fertilizers, other fertilizers are forced on the cultivators. This practice dampens the demand from the farmers.

A Viable Fertilizer Depot

A sub-depot holder is paid by the Punjab Cooperative Marketing and Supply Federation a net commission of Rs 12 to Rs 30 per tonne on different fertilizers. On an average, he gets roughly Rs 20 per tonne. All other expenses of storage, sortage, handling, transportation and other incidental charges are paid in addition.

For a one man sub-depot, the operator would need to handle 152.4 tonnes of fertilizers in a year to earn a reasonable amount of commission (we assume Rs 250 per month). The present level of fertilizer consumption in Punjab (1969-70) being 41.90 kilos per hectare, a viable one man depot can be set up for 331 hectares (say for 330 to 350 hectares) of cropped area.

Fertilizer Response and Recommendations. Sound fertilizer recommendations are always formulated after giving due weight to economic considerations of fertilizer use. It is profitable to use fertilizers only when their cost is covered by the additional returns. Since the prices of crops and fertilizers are subject to change, the recommendations need a continual review.

Based on the experiments conducted by the Departments of Soils and Plant Breeding of the Punjab Agricultural University, some economic optima for fertilizer use (nitrogen and phosphorus) have been worked out for wheat and bajra. With the help of production functions the optimum yield for each variety has also been calculated.

The data are drawn from both University Experimental Stations and from experiments on cultivators' fields. Since the cultivation of high-yielding varieties is of recent origin and is yet to stabilize, recommendations based on these experiments under controlled conditions need to be used with caution. The following production functions were used:

$$X = a + bx - ax^2 \quad \text{(quadratic)}$$
$$Y = a + b\sqrt{x - ax} \quad \text{(square root quadratic)}$$

The analysis was further carried out with the function that gave the best fit. The optimum doses were worked out at varying product prices, i.e., Rs 75, Rs 80 and Rs 90 per quintal in case of wheat and Rs 62, Rs 72 and Rs 82 in case of bajra. The present prices of fertilizers taken for analysis were Rs 2.55 per kilo of N, Rs 2.68 per kilo of P_2O_5 and Re 0.85 per kilo of K_2O.

Fertilizer Prices. The input prices in India are the highest in the world. This is especially so in the case of fertilizers. In the U.S.A. and Japan, for example, a farmer can purchase one kilo of fertilizer (NPK content) with 1.5 kilos of paddy or 2.7 kilos of paddy respectively or 1.7 kilos of wheat respectively, while our farmer has to pay the price of 5.2 kilos of paddy or 3.7 kilos of wheat. This ratio is more favourable even in neighbouring Pakistan where a farmer has to pay the equivalent of only 0.85 kilo of rice for one kilo of fertilizer (nitrogen).

The comparison with different countries can be seen from Table 31.

Table 31

Prices of rice and wheat in different countries and quantity of these commodities equal in value to one kilogram of fertilizer

	1962-63	US cents	Kilograms
Rice (paddy)	Japan	15.6	1.2
	United States	13.6	1.5
	Philippines	7.8	3.4
	China (Taiwan)	9.0	3.5
	Thailand	5.6	4.1
	India	6.6	5.2
	United Arab Republic	4.9	7.1
Wheat	Japan	11.6	1.7
	Spain	9.3	2.3
	Netherlands	8.6	2.4
	United States	7.3	2.7
	India	9.4	3.7
	United Arab Republic	5.8	6.0

Source: *The State of Food and Agriculture*, 1967 (FAO), p. III.

Also, the available data show that the physical production response to fertilizers in India is much lower compared to that in many other countries such as the U.S.A. and Japan. This further increases the cost of fertilizers to the farmers in India. It is therefore desirable to have a look at the price structure of fertilizers in India and bring it down to the level where its use can be enhanced economically and considerably. This will be of great benefit to the small farmers who are now being deterred from using fertilizers because of their meagre resources.

17. Electricity

Poor in mineral fuels, Punjab is comparatively lucky to have potentialities to harness the perennial water flow for hydro-electric development. As long as snow and rain fall in the Himalayas and as long as the water runs in the Sutlej, Beas and Ravi, Punjab will have at its disposal a perpetual source of electric power. How much of this water is conserved and utilized will reflect on the prosperity of the state. The present trend of demand shows that maximum efforts have to be made to harness the waters of these rivers to meet the increasing demands of mechanical power for agriculture and industry. Coal and oil, in time, will go, but hydro-electric power will remain. So great has its importance become that its consumption is considered an index of prosperity. Electric power is playing a vital role in the development of different sectors of the economy. In agriculture, it supplies the mechanical power to the tube-wells, pumping-sets, threshers and chaff-cutters. Its importance is paramount in providing perennial irrigation in areas not served by the canals. The rapid mechanization of agriculture is making a staggering demand for mechanical power. Being much cheaper than mineral fuel, the demand for electric power is fast increasing.

In Punjab, agriculture stands next to the industrial sector in the consumption of electric power and this consumption is rapidly increasing. For irrigation alone the per capita electric consumption has gone up from 0.03 KWH in 1951 to 10.86 KWH in 1968. In comparison with other states of India, Punjab stands conspicuously high in electric power consumption (Table 32).

Table 32
Annual per capita consumption of electricity for irrigation, 1967-68

S. No.	State	Consumption in KWH
1.	Tamil Nadu	27.93
2.	Haryana	11.78
3.	Punjab	10.86
4.	Gujarat	8.98
5.	Andhra Pradesh	6.03
6.	Uttar Pradesh	4.15
7.	Maharashtra	3.31
8.	Mysore	3.28
9.	Kerala	1.85
10.	Rajasthan	1.55
11.	Jammu & Kashmir	1.13
12.	Bihar	1.13
13.	Assam	0.69
14.	Madhya Pradesh	0.55
15.	West Bengal	0.26
16.	Orissa	0.16
	India	5.03

Source: *Statistical Abstract of Punjab*, 1969.

Not only the per capita consumption for irrigation is increasing but the share of the agriculture sector as a whole is expanding. In 1960 agriculture consumed 15 per cent of the total electric power; the share had risen to 35 per cent in 1970. Table 33 shows the energy generated and consumed in agriculture during the last one decade.

Table 33
Electric power generated and consumed in Punjab

Year	Total energy generated (share of Punjab)	Energy utilized (in Punjab only)	Energy utilized for agri- culture only	Percentage consump- tion in agriculture
	Mkwh	Mkwh	Mkwh	
1960-61	987.74	488.23	72.91	14.9
1961-62	1849.62	569.48	80.28	14.2
1962-63	2368.90	673.04	84.23	12.5
1963-64	2980.86	836.36	108.62	13.0
1964-65	3200.74	964.68	122.26	12.7
1965-66	3406.07	1096.26	210.58	19.3
1966-67	3802.47	1204.67	257.01	21.2
1967-68	*2227.05	728.19	188.78	25.2
1968-69	2446.98	783.24	229.24	29.3
1969-70	2781.23	758.68	268.16	35.6

Source: Punjab State Electricity Board.
*Figures relate to the reorganized Punjab.

The phenomenal increase in electric consumption in the agricultural sector is attributed to the fact that the need to extend irrigational facilities became very acute with the introduction of high-yielding dwarf wheat varieties. To fulfil the demand, the Punjab State Electricity Board launched a crash programme of tube-well energization in May 1967. Since then it has achieved considerable success in this direction. Table 34 shows the number of tube-wells energized in the pre-organized and reorganized Punjab and the targets fixed for the fourth five year plan.

Table 34
Number of tube-wells energized and targets fixed

Year	No. of tube-wells working with electricity in pre-organized Punjab	No. of tube-wells working with electricity in reorganized Punjab	Target fixed for energization (Nos.)	Target achieved in energization (Nos.)
1950-51		—	—	—
1951-52		—	—	—
1952-53	Data not available	—	—	—
1953-54		—	—	—
1954 55		—	—	—
1955-56	3,840	—	—	—
1956-57	5,460	—	—	—
1957-58	7,165	—	—	—
1958-59	8,699	—	—	—
1959-60	10,282	—	—	—
1960-61	12,054	—	—	—
1961-62	14,256	—	—	—
1962-63	17,459	—	—	—
1963-64	22,785	—.	—	—
1964-65	29,684	—	—	—
1965-66	41,085	25,296	—	—
1966-67	53,648	31,876	—	—
1967-68	—	41,960	—	—
1968-69	—	59,112	—	—
1969-70	—	79,036	20,000	19,924
1970-71	—	—	20,000	—
1971-72	—	—	25,000	—
1972-73	—	—	25,000	—
1973-74	—	—	30,000	—

Source: Punjab State Electricity Board.

The district-wise break-up of tube-wells energized up to 31 March 1970 is given in Table 35.

Table 35

Distribution of tube-wells working with electric power

S. No.	District	No. of tube-wells		
		Up to 31.3.70	From 1.4.69 to 31.3.70	Grand Total as on 31.3.70
1.	Jullundur	9,725	3,214	12,939
2.	Ludhiana	9,892	2,629	12,521
3.	Amritsar	6,744	2,503	9,247
4.	Ferozepur	6,419	2,760	9,179
5.	Patiala	5,763	2,290	8,053
6.	Gurdaspur	5,149	1,906	7,055
7.	Sangrur	4,995	1,223	6,218
8.	Hoshiarpur	4,692	1,502	6.194
9.	Kapurthala	2,365	1,196	3,561
10.	Ropar	2,166	317	2,483
11.	Bhatinda	1,202	384	1,586
	Total	**59,112**	**19,924**	**79,036**

Source: Punjab State Electricity Board.

In spite of the best efforts of the State Electricity Board, a balance could not be achieved in the demand and supply of power in the agricultural sector. This can be judged from the fact that the number of pending applications for new connections is multiplying. In 1967, there were 24,406 pending applications and the number rose to 41,984 in 1968 and to 53,822 in 1969.

There are a number of physical handicaps which are to be removed in order to bridge the gap between demand and supply. The gap is becoming so acute that these problems need immediate attention.

The cost of energy at 11 Kv Bus, i.e., the grid rate for the combined power system for Punjab works out to be 6.42 paise. The tariff applicable to the tube-well consumers on a flat rate basis since 1968 is as given below:

1. Tube-wells up to 5 bhp   Rs 7 per bhp
2. Tube-wells 5 to 7.5 bhp   Rs 7.5 per bhp
3. Tube-wells 7.5 to 10 bhp   Rs 8 per bhp

4. Tube-wells 10 to 12 bhp   Rs 8.5 per bhp
5. Tube-wells above 12 bhp   Rs 9 per bhp

Over and above these flat rates, there is a demand charge of one rupee for every bhp.

The revenue returns from the tube-wells are very low, taking into account the huge capital investment the electricity board has to make for the energization of tube-wells. Tube-well energization is thus an uneconomical programme.

The second difficulty of the board is the paucity of funds. Total funds required for the energization of 120,000 tube-wells during the fourth plan are Rs 60 crores. This is a huge sum and cannot be made available under ordinary circumstances. Either the Punjab Government has to come forward or the board has to run for a big loan to achieve the fourth five year plan target.

Another difficulty in the energization of tube-wells is the overloading of some transmission lines which results in frequent breakdowns. This has occurred mainly because of a sharp rise in the demand for tube-wells. The State Electricity Board is striving hard to improve the system by augmentation of the existing sub-stations and by taking up new works on a planned basis. A master plan has been drawn up for the transmission network of the state keeping in view its future requirements and load growth. In order to complete the design work and procurement of material and equipment well in advance, a phased annual plan has also been drawn up to 1973-74.

The biggest problem at present, however, is the non-availability of adequate power. The existing sources of power are a share from the Bhakra-Nangal complex, Shanan Power House, Nangal Thermal Power House and purchase from Talwara. The total availability from these sources is 170 MW. The demand for power has already exceeded the generating capacity and the maximum demand touched in May 1970 was 341 MW against the firm power of 170 MW. The trend does not seem to turn favourable in the near future. The availability of power from various sources and the power requirements based on load forecast approved by CW and PC in the fifth annual power survey are given in Table 36.

Table 36
Availability and demand for power in Punjab

S. No.	Detail	1970-71	1971-72	1972-73	1973-74
1.	Power availability (MW)	233	439	542	661
2.	Maximum power (MW) demand	502	611	735	871
3.	Power deficit (MW)	—269	—172	—193	—210

Source: Punjab State Electricity Board.

From Table 36 it is clear that the power famine is likely to remain serious in the coming years.

In order to meet the future power demand of the state, a number of generation projects have been started or are proposed for the fourth five year plan period. Table 37 gives the installed capacities and target dates of commissioning of such projects.

Table 37
Proposed electric generating schemes

S. No.	Name of the scheme	Unit/PH	Installed capacity	Target date of commissioning
1.	UBDC Hydel Scheme Stage-1	I PH	15 MW	Nov. 1970
		II PH	15 MW	Mar. 1971
		III PH	15 MW	Sept. 1971
2.	Guru Nanak Thermal Plant	I Unit	110 MW	Oct. 1972
		II Unit	110 MW	Oct. 1973
3.	Shanan Renovation		36 MW	to 1973-74
			48 MW	
4.	Shanan Extension		50 MW	1975-76
5.	Diesel and Thermal Sets		95 MW	1970-72
6.	Guru Nanak Thermal Extension Unit		200 MW	1976-77

Source: Punjab State Electricity Board.

The State Electricity Board also proposes to purchase power from other sources given in Table 38.

The other inter-state projects in which the state has a share and which will be completed during the fifth five year plan period are given in Table 39.

Table 38
Anticipated sources for the purchase of electric power

S. No.	Name of source	Power to be purchased (MW)	Date from which power will be made available
1.	Pong Thermal Station	4	Being purchased since 1968-69
2.	Bassi Power Station	3	1970-71
3.	Nuclear Power Plant, Kota	100	1971-72
4.	Badarpur Thermal Station	60	1971-72

Source: Punjab State Electricity Board.

Table 39
Anticipated share of power in the inter-state electric projects

S. No.	Name of the project	Power availability to Punjab (MW)	Likely date of power availability
1.	Beas Project Unit I & II	84	1974-75
2.	Bhakra Nangal Project	137 to 200	—
3.	Baira Suil Project	85	1975-76
4.	Slal Project	80	1976-77
5.	Thein Dam Project	93	1978-79

Source: Punjab State Electricity Board.

Nuclear Power Station. After having utilized the major hydro resources in and around the state and having expanded the thermal generation to the maximum limit of economy, the only source left to be tapped for the state is nuclear power. The demand for electric power is increasing at such a high rate that it is almost certain that the gap between supply and demand will not be filled without a nuclear power house. If a nuclear plant is installed during the fifth five year plan, it will afford great relief to the state from the chronic power shortages. Already the supply deficit has reached a state where it is adversely affecting agricultural development.

The unexpected power crisis which occurred so seriously during the year 1970-71, and which is likely to remain at the same intensity, is not the result of wrong planning by the State Electricity Board, but is a result of the delay involved in commissioning the Central Government projects, including the

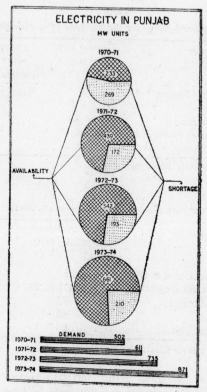

Fig. 11 Electricity in Punjab, MW
units—demand and availability.

nuclear power plant at Kota, and the Badarpur thermal station. These projects were originally scheduled to be commissioned in 1970-71 and Punjab expected to get 160 MW from these two sources. The Bassi power house, which was scheduled to be commissioned during 1969-70, and from which power was to be purchased, has so far not been commissioned. The lack of large quantities of water in Gobind Sagar has aggravated the situation further. The water level in September 1970 stood at about 30.4 metres below the corresponding level in September 1970.

Being fully alive to the present difficult power position in the state, the board is exploring all possible sources to obtain power to meet the needs. Arrangements have been made with the Madhya Pradesh State Electricity Board for purchasing 50 MW power from the Satpura thermal plant. Power is also being purchased from Rajasthan to the extent of 20 MW. As the possible relief from various Central as well as state projects is not likely to materialize before 1972-73, the Punjab State Electricity Board has decided to install 47 diesel generating sets in a year's time.

18. Mechanization of Agriculture

The process of mechanization of agriculture has to be viewed in the context of the overall objective of increased agricultural production. The extensive irrigation system, more particularly the developing network of tube-wells, has made large-scale adoption of high-yielding varieties feasible in Punjab. It has simultaneously made multi-cropping a practical proposal. In the next decade, a substantial increase in agricultural production in Punjab is expected with at least two crops being raised on irrigated land. With tube-well irrigation, the intensity of cropping could even be more than 200 per cent. However, a serious limitation has set in because of the reduced time gaps between harvesting and threshing of one crop and the sowing of the next. The raising of two or more crops in a year will be practical only through mechanization of these operations and further development of tube-well irrigation. In fact, the need for mechanization has already overtaken the state's agricultural planning, and shortages of major ingredients, such as tractors, machinery and power for lifting water have become serious bottlenecks in agricultural progress.

Mechanization has also led to the proper utilization of inputs, like fertilizers, pesticides and water. This aspect is, however, not fully appreciated. It is well established that with the use of modern equipment, the utilization efficiency of these inputs is substantially increased. For instance, a farmer having a tractor and a blade terracer manages to grade his land to a much better level in course of time, as compared to the farmer not having similar sources of power and equipment at his disposal. Proper grading helps in reducing water losses during irrigation. Among many other useful aids are the seed-cum-fertilizer drill and well designed plant-protection equipment.

A prerequisite for mechanization is the availability of sufficient power which is the nucleus of all technological developments. The state of progress in industry or agriculture is fairly and accurately represented by the power use index. Recent studies have indicated that per capita energy used in India is the lowest in the world. This explains why our country is poor. Figure 12 presents the situation visually.

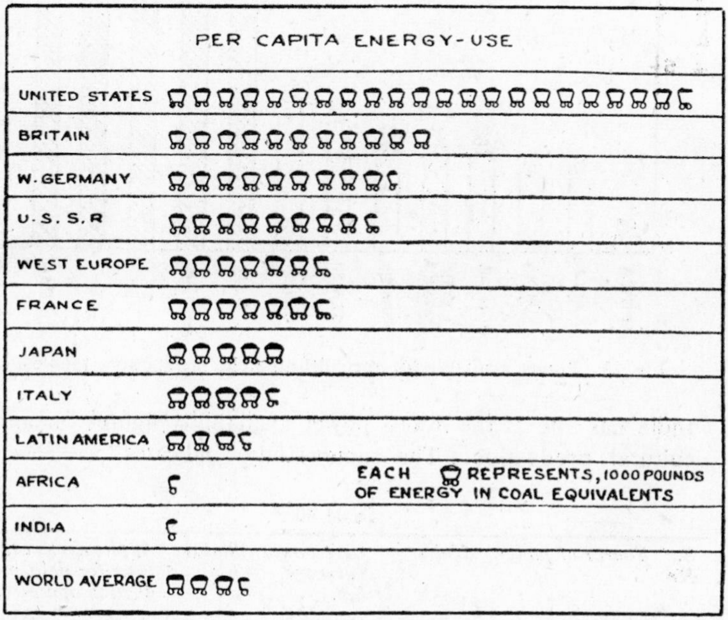

Fig. 12 World energy consumption—per capita energy use.

Another study conducted by a sub-panel of the President's Science Advisory Committee (United States of America) has brought out a comparative statement of power available for agricultural field production for the year 1964-65 for different countries of the world.

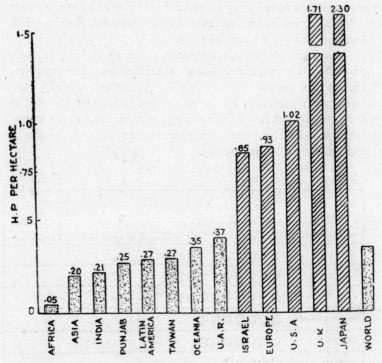

Fig. 13   Power available for agricultural field production, 1964-65.

India has one of the lowest power availability figures for agricultural production. The same study indicates a definite

Table 40

S. No.	Source of power	Units	Unit power (average h.p.)	Total h.p.	Applications other than for field production operations
1.	Human	1,938,000	0.067	129,200	post-harvest handling of produce, farmstead jobs.
2.	Bullocks	1,400,000	0.5	700,000	Irrigation, transport threshing, transport irrigation.
3.	Tractors*				
	Total			1,379,200	

Source: 1.   *Statistical Abstract*, Punjab.
            2.   *Indian Agric. in Brief*, IX Ed.
*Units estimated in March 1970.

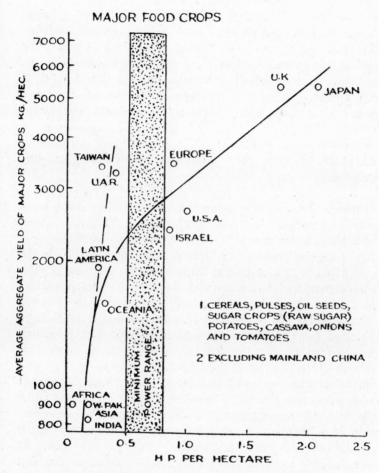

Fig. 14   Relationship between yield and power input.

correlation between the power available for crop production operations (excluding irrigation) and the yield. The situation is presented graphically in Figure 14.

Table 40 gives the extent of power available from different sources for agricultural production operations in Punjab.

Table 40 indicates that bullocks continue to be the major source of power for agricultural production operations (excluding irrigation). An estimated 80 per cent of the total power is available for these operations. The average availability of power for agricultural production operations (excluding irrigation) for the net sown area of 3,886,000 hectares therefore stands at 0.28 h.p./hectare. To bring it to a reasonable level of one horse power per hectare, which would be the minimum requirement to achieve an acceptable level of agricultural production in the next ten years, an additional 0.75 h.p. per hectare will have to be made available for agricultural operations (excluding irrigation).

Tractors. This additional power will have to come mostly from small and medium sized four wheel tractors. The total number of holdings in the state is 724,365. Out of these, 69,365 holdings fall in the size group of 12 hectares and above, 320,000 in the group four to 12 hectares and the rest under four hectares. The present trend leads to the assumption that by 1980 all the holdings in the first group and a substantial percentage of those in the second group will be mechanized. The number of really large holdings being rather small in the state, most of the tractors needed for agricultural mechanization will be from the medium (about 30 h.p.) and small size (about 20 h.p. or less). The very small four wheel tractors (substantially under 15 h.p.) are neither economical nor capable of handling different operations under the accepted cropping patterns and intensities. The mechanization of the holdings in the third group will, therefore, depend greatly on the extent of development of custom operation. At a reasonable estimate 225,000 to 250,000 holdings (the first group, and about half the second group) will be operated with tractors. Presuming that there will not be any substantial change in the number of men engaged in agriculture and that the number of bullocks will go down owing to partial replacement by the tractors, Table 41 projects the source of power for agricultural production (excluding irrigation) in the year 1980.

Part of the energy supplied by the above sources will be used for purposes other than agricultural field production operations. However, if 75 to 80 per cent of this power is available for agricul-

Table 41

S. No.	Source	Units	Units power (h.p.)	Total (h.p.)
1.	Human	2,000,000	0.67	134,000
2.	Bullocks	1,000,000	0.5	500,000
3.	Tractors	230,000	.22	5,060,000
	Total			5,694,000

tural production operations, the criterion of one h.p. per hectare over the four million hectares expected to be under cultivation in 1980 will be met.

The above analysis brings out that nearly 200,000 additional tractors will be in operation by 1980. Taking into consideration the requirements for new additions and replacements of the old tractors, a production capacity of 30,000 tractors per year will be needed to meet the needs of this state alone. There is an immediate need for reviewing and planning tractor manufacture in at least two sizes, i.e. 15 to 20 h.p. and 30 h.p. in sufficient numbers in Punjab. At least three good sized tractor-manufacturing units are required to be set up in the state to meet the demand by 1980.

Until now, the replacement or substitution influence of agricultural mechanization has been oriented more towards bullocks than labour. Operations like threshing and seed-bed preparation are examples of this. Recently, however, there has been a definite demand by the farmers for mechanization of labour-intensive operations like the harvesting of wheat and groundnut, and planting and harvesting of potato. This appears to be substantially due to rising wages and shortage of agricultural labour at peak periods. The possibilities of partial unemployment of agricultural labour due to large-scale mechanization of wheat harvesting through combines, as an example, cannot be overlooked. Advance and careful planning needs to be done to work out the extent to which the mechanization of labour-intensive operations could be allowed in the state during the next ten years or so. Proper control on the mechanization of such operations and its beneficial influence in terms of higher cropping intensities and cultivation of crops like potato over larger areas (the production of which, even when reasonably mechanized, is more labour-intensive than that of cereals) could eliminate the danger of unemployment. The combination of labour-intensive operations and better power-machinery systems for maintaining satisfactory levels of employment in agriculture and at the same time achieving high production per unit area and per worker through mechanization is not impracticable. The following chart presents such situations already existing in other countries.

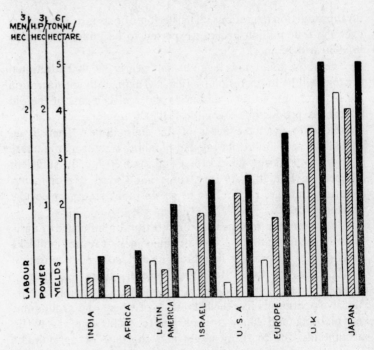

Fig. 15　Labour, power, and yield per hectare.

Machinery. The availability of proper equipment for different operations should keep pace with the addition of new tractors. There is substantial scope for improving the operational efficiency of the bullock-operated units also by supplying suitable equipment to the farmers. The estimated availability of different types of farm machinery used in 1969 has been worked out and the investment on machinery per hectare in the state comes to less than Rs 200 (Table 42). This is much below the levels of investment on machinery per hectare in countries like West Germany and Japan where intensive farming is practised. This investment for West German farms under 100 hectares stands at Rs 1,500 per hectare and for Japan Rs 600 per hectare.

Table 42

Estimated number of different types of farm equipment in use in Punjab in 1969

S. No.	Item	No. in use	Investment (Rs)
1.	Disk plough (tractors)	2,000	3,000,000
2.	Mouldboard ploughs (tractor)	500	750,000
3.	Mouldboard and iron ploughs (bullocks)	650,000	9,750,000
4.	Wooden ploughs	700,000	7,000,000
5.	Disk harrow (tractor)	5,000	7,500,000
6.	Disk harrow (bullock)	25,000	5,000,000
7.	Cultivators (tractor)	12,000	12,000,000
8.	Cultivators (bullocks)	50,000	1,500,000
9.	Blade terracers (tractors)	5,000	3,000,000
10.	Hydraulic levellers or land planes (tractors)	50	100,000
11.	Seed-drills (tractor)	1,500	1,800,000
12.	Seed-drills (bullocks)	12,000	3,600,000
13.	Planters (tractor) seed and potato	130	300,000
14.	Planters (bullocks)	500	75,000
15.	Plant-protection equipment (power)	750	750,000
16.	Plant-protection equipment (manual)	20,000	4,000,000
17.	Reapers and binders	40	150,000
18.	Combines	—	—
19.	Groundnut harvesters	30	60,000
20.	Potato harvesters	—	—
21.	Threshers	80,000	80,000,000
22.	Transport trailers	10,000	15,000,000
23.	Bullock-carts	500,000	250,000,000
24.	Tractors	13,000	156,000,000
25.	Pumping-sets	80,000	200,000,000
	Total		761,000,000

Unless efficient and matching equipment for different operations is made available in sufficient quantities to the farmers, the tractor power available with the farmers will be wasted to a very great extent. The large-scale use of self-propelled equipment for many years to come will in general not be justified.

There will be tremendous scope for making full use of the tractor power itself after tractors are made available to the farmers in large numbers for different operations. Tying up a costly power unit with a machine used for one operation only for a limited period during a year, as it happens in self-propelled machinery, will not be economically justified on a large scale. The question of large self-propelled combines versus tractor-mounted/pulled smaller combines may have to be reviewed in this context. The estimated requirements of machinery for different holding sizes has been given in Tables 43 to 46 and the estimate of the number of major items of farm machinery expected to be in use by 1980 is given in Table 47.

Table 43*

Projected need for equipment in 1980 on holdings of four to 12 hectares having bullocks as the source of power for field operations

S. No.	Item	Quantity	Remarks
1.	Mouldboard plough	2	1. Some operations like land levelling and part of harvesting will be done through custom operation.
2.	Disk harrow	1	
3.	Seed-cum-fertilizer drill	1	
4.	Planter**	1	
5.	Cultivator with attachments	1	
6.	Sprayer (power)**	1	2. All holdings will not be equipped to this level and on this pattern. The average level of equipment ownership in this group may reach only 60% of the level indicated here.
7.	Groundnut digger	1	
8.	Reaper**	1	
9.	Corn sheller (power)	1	
10.	Drummy thresher	1	
11.	Pumping-set	1	
12.	Bullock-cart with pneumatic tires	1	
13.	Hand tools	2 sets	

* Projected on the basis of a cropping intensity of 200 per cent.
**Operations likely to be handled on custom basis also.

The use of farm equipment worth more than Rs 500 crores by 1980 in the state would require a well organized repair and maintenance service in the state. The following pattern should be considered for developing this service as part of the programme of the Agro-Industries Corporation.

Table 44*

Projected need for equipment in 1980 on 50 per cent holdings of four to 12 hectares having a small tractor as the source of power for field operations

S. No.	Item	Quantity	Remarks
1.	Tractor 20 h.p. or less	1	1. Some operations, like harvesting, will be done through custom operations. Many holdings will not have specialized equipment like potato planter and digger.
2.	Levelling blade	1	
3.	Disk plough**	1	
4.	Disk harrow	1	
5.	Tool bar with attachments	1	
6.	Seed-cum-fertilizer drill**	1	
7.	Corn planter**	1	
8.	Potato planter—single row	1	2. The average level of equipment ownership in this group may reach 60 per cent only of the level indicated here.
9.	Sprayer (power/tractor**)	1	
10.	Reaper**	1	
11.	Groundnut digger	1	
12.	Potato digger	1	
13.	Power corn sheller-husker	1	
14.	Thresher	1	
15.	Trailer	1	
16.	Pumps	1	
17.	Hand tools	2 sets	

* Projected on the basis of a cropping intensity of 200 per cent.
**Operations likely to be handled on custom basis also.

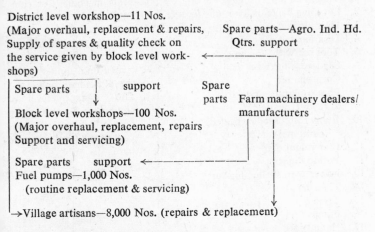

District level workshop—11 Nos.
(Major overhaul, replacement & repairs,   Spare parts—Agro. Ind. Hd.
Supply of spares & quality check on   Qtrs. support
the service given by block level work- ←————————
shops)

Spare parts   support   Spare
                                                parts   Farm machinery dealers/
Block level workshops—100 Nos.   manufacturers
(Major overhaul, replacement, repairs
Support and servicing)

Spare parts   support ←———————
Fuel pumps—1,000 Nos.
    (routine replacement & servicing)

→Village artisans—8,000 Nos. (repairs & replacement)

In addition, small workshops undertaking farm machinery repairs in all towns should be encouraged to improve their facilities for providing quality service to the farmers.

Farm Machinery Design and Testing Centre. By 1980 an additional investment of Rs 500 crores or more will be made by Punjabi farmers in farm machinery and tractors. By standards set for industrial research one per cent of this investment, i.e. five crore rupees should be made available for farm machinery design development, research and testing from 1970 to 1980. This money should be used to finance a strong farm machinery research programme at Punjab Agricultural University. This investment is essential to ensure that suitable equipment is developed in time to meet the requirements of mechanization and that the future investment in farm equipment is made useful. Testing of farm machinery in the state should be combined with the research programme at the P.A.U. and should aim at helping the farmer in the selection of equipment and the manufacturer in improving the quality of his product.

Table 45*

Projected need for equipment in 1980 on holdings of 12 hectares or more having tractors as a source of power for field operations

S. No.	Item	Quantity	Remarks
1.	Tractor 30 h.p.	1	1. Some machines like combines might be used for custom operation. Other machines like potato planter and digger will be owned on a limited number of holdings only.
2.	Levelling blade or hydraulic leveller	1	
3.	Disk plough	1	
4.	Disk harrow	1	
5.	Tool bar with attachments	1	
6.	Seed-cum-fertilizer drill	1	
7.	Corn planter	1	
8.	Potato planter—two row	1	2. The average level of equipment in this group may reach only 60 per cent of the level indicated here.
9.	Sprayer (tractor)**	1	
10.	Reaper/mounted or trailed combine harvester**	1	
11.	Groundnut digger	11	
12.	Potato digger	1	
13.	Power corn sheller husker	1	
14.	Thresher	1	
15.	Trailer	1	
16.	Pumps	1	
17.	Hand tools	—	

* Projected on the basis of a cropping intensity of 200 per cent.
**Operations likely to be handled on custom basis also.

Table 46*

Projected need for equipment in 1980 on holdings of 20 hectares and above

S. No.	Item	Quantity	Remarks
1.	Tractor 50 h.p.	1 or	1. Specialized equipment like potato planters and diggers will be owned on a limited number of farms.
2.	Hydraulic leveller	1 more	
3.	Plough	1	
4.	Harrow	1	
5.	Tool bar with attachments	1	
6.	Seed-cum-fertilizer drill	1	2. Few very large farms may go in for self-propelled combines.
7.	Corn planter	1	
8.	Potato planter—two row	1	
9.	Sprayer (tractor)	1	
10.	Mounted or trailed combine**	1	
11.	Groundnut digger	1	
12.	Potato digger	1	
13.	Corn stripper	1	
14.	Corn husker-sheller	1	
15.	Trailer	1 or more	
16.	Pumping-sets	—	
17.	Hand tools	—	

* Projected on the basis of a cropping intensity of 200 per cent.
**Operations likely to be handled on custom basis also.

Table 47*

Major items of farm machinery expected to be in use by 1980

S. No.	Item	No.
1.	Tractors 50 h.p.	17,000
2.	Tractors 30 h.p.	52,000
3.	Tractors 15-20 h.p.	165,000
4.	Seed-cum-fertilizer drills (animal drawn)	100,000
5.	Seed-cum-fertilizer drills (tractors)	100,000
6.	Planters (bullocks)	50,000
7.	Planters (tractors)	50,000
8.	Levelling blades	100,000
9.	Disk harrow (bullocks)	200,000
10.	Disk ploughs (tractor)	100,000
11.	Disk harrow (tractors)	150,000
12.	Tool bars (tractors)	150,000
13.	Sprayers (power)	100,000
14.	Threshers/combines	200,000
15.	Pumping-sets	350,000
16.	Carts with pneumatic tires	400,000
17.	Trailers	200,000

*Projected on the basis of a cropping intensity of 200 per cent.

The manufacture of farm machinery in Punjab is in the hands of small fabricating units. In 1968-69, 400 such units were registered with the Agriculture Department for purposes of getting loans and supply of scarce raw material, etc. These units led by enterprising men have played a very useful role in the development and mechanization of Punjab's agriculture, but they operate under the major constraints of limited finance, limited raw materials and scarce power. Because of their small size, most of these units cannot make use of modern production techniques and tools; cannot exercise quality control and lack proper sales and service organization. To ensure growth and development of the state's farm machinery industry and simultaneously the supply of quality equipment to the farmer, the manufacturing units should be encouraged to take up specialization and develop mutual cooperation. This is feasible if these units are grouped together in the industrial areas. The facilities for testing and quality control should be pooled for such groups, as otherwise few of these units can develop them individually. Given the required support, the farm machinery industry in the state can develop very fast and therefore its space requirements should be kept in view in future industrial planning.

19. Roads for Food

Roads are commonly called arteries through which the lifeblood of an economy flows; they are the key to the development of an economy, and catalysts in the transformation of an economy from poverty to prosperity. Economic development is the technological transformation of the economy, not only in skill and labour but also in space and location, and roads are the essential elements in this transformation. As Wilfred Owen observes:

Transport is a necessary ingredient of nearly every aspect of economic and social development. It plays a key role in getting land into production, in marketing agricultural commodities, and in making forest and mineral wealth accessible. It is a significant factor in the development of industry, in the expansion of trade, in the conduct of health and education programs, and in the exchange of ideas.*

Once a village is linked by a pucka road with a town its economy undergoes a remarkable transformation. The farmers market their produce with facility, and are also enabled to purchase fertilizers, plant-protection chemicals and agricultural implements from the market town with ease. This leads to rapid changes in agriculture. Villagers who have had no experience of growing commercial crops like potatoes and vegetables adopt them easily. Roads also promote industry directly as well as indirectly.

*Wilfred Owen, *Strategy for Mobility*, Washington, 1964, p. 1.

Villagers who have never used bicycles purchase them once they have the facility of a road. Tractors can command larger areas for cultivation along the roads, and custom ploughing is also promoted. Besides, the sons and daughters of the farmers are enabled to take advantage of educational facilities in the towns.

The construction of roads in Punjab, especially to serve the rural population, was never taken seriously under the British. Even at a very conservative rate of road construction, what the British did in 100 years was accomplished in the first 15 years of independence. Until recently the State Government was concerned with the national and state highways only, and minor roads, so important to the rural masses, were in the jurisdiction of the district boards, which chronically suffer from a paucity of funds.

For the first time an attempt to undertake a road construction programme as a national project was made in 1943 when the Nagpur Plan was formulated. One of the objectives of this plan was to bring every village of India within 3.2 kilometres of a road in a period of 20 years. The target was subsequently revised in 1958 and it was proposed that during the period 1961-1981, every village in an agricultural area should be within 2.4 kilometres of a road. Not to speak of achievements, even these targets were too humble to be compared with some of the countries in western Europe. Road construction did not make any significant headway in the first 15 years of our planning. During the first five year plan period less than 1,800 kilometres of roads were constructed in Punjab. In other words, in a span of five years, only 3.68 kilometres of roads were added to every 256 square kilometres in Punjab. During the second and third plan periods, 2,996 and 2,121 kilometres were constructed, adding only 6.24 and 4.48 kilometres respectively in each of these plan periods.

The slow pace of road construction during the three plan periods did not make a perceptible impact on the social and economic life of the rural masses. In the Community Development Programme also, the construction of metalled roads was not adequately emphasized. As a result, the barrier of distance standing in the way of village communities to come into the

Table 48

Roads constructed in Punjab (kilometres)

S. No.	Year	Length of roads constructed		
		Per year	During plan period	Per 256 square kilometres
1.	1951-52	280		
2.	1952-53	233.6		
3.	1953-54	147.2		
4.	1954-55	180.8		
5.	1955-56	913.6	1,755.2	3.66
6.	1956-57	646.4		
7.	1957-58	504		
8.	1958-59	553.6		
9.	1959-60	662.4		
10.	1960-61	627.2	2,993.6	6.24
11.	1961-62	550		
12.	1962-63	376		
13.	1963-64	288		
14.	1964-65	339.2		
15.	1965-66	568	2,281.6	4.48
16.	1966-67*	160		
17.	1967-68	251.2		
18.	1968-69	1,168		
19.	1969-70	1,920	3,499.2	17.92

Source: Unpublished records, Office of the Chief Engineer, B&R, Punjab.

*Figures pertain to the reorganized Punjab.

mainstream of the national development process could not be broken.

Crash Programme for Rural Link Roads. The situation changed after the reorganization of Punjab. The present State of Punjab was the agricultural core of bigger Punjab before 1966. Without minerals and forests the future prosperity of the new state was bound to be determined by farm land. The government's policies were therefore given a rural orientation. The diversion of state and public financial and material resources, reclamation of waste-lands, development of irrigation facilities and, coincidently the introduction of high-yielding dwarf wheat varieties resulted in a tremendous increase in farm production which was much in excess of local needs. This extraordinary development which occurred in a very short period created the problem of marketing of the surplus farm produce. To cope with the situation, the need was felt for new marketing centres to sell farm produce at the nearest place, in the shortest time and in the easiest manner. What was required was not merely more markets but more roads to link farms with markets.

The State Government realized that it was not a simple question of quickly carting the harvest to the markets but also of providing the farms with more fertilizers, better seeds, improved implements and technical know-how. If roads to rural areas were not provided as quickly as possible the future agricultural development would suffer. To meet these demands, the State Government launched a crash programme for the construction of village roads in 1968. No other development programme received such unanimous support from the rural people as the road construction plan, and the benefits have been tremendous—economic, social and cultural—to all sections of the village community.

Encouraged by the popularity of the programme and noting the impact on the economy and life of the village, the State Government felt that the tempo of the road construction pro-gramme should be kept up. As a result the number of road rollers in the state increased from 90 in 1968 to 160 in 1970, and during 1969-70, 1,920 kilometres of roads were built. This alone is more than the roads added in the whole of the first plan period in undivided Punjab. The increase in kilometreage since 1968 has materially changed the road accessibility and intensity in the state, visible not only when seen in the time perspective but also in comparison with other parts of India.

Accessibility to Roads. There has been a substantial improvement in the accessibility of roads during the period 1950-1970. In 1950, accessibility to the metalled roads was the worst in southern Punjab. This area was a part of erstwhile Pepsu where little development took place in the field of road cons-truction. Not to speak of the villages, even important market towns like Mansa and Budhlada were far away from metalled roads. Bhatinda, which was the second important city of the

erstwhile Patiala State, was not on the road map in 1950. Much
of the area of southern Ferozepore and Bhatinda districts was
more than 48 kilometres away from any metalled roads. In
northern Punjab, the position was comparatively better and
the maximum distance of villages from roads was less than 26
kilometres confined mainly to the sub-Siwalik dissected parts
of the state.

By 1960 (Fig. 16) many roads had penetrated into these areas
and road accessibility had greatly increased. No part of the
state remained beyond a distance of 12.8 kilometres except a
few tracts in south-western Ferozepore district and a few smaller
ones in other parts of the state. By 1971 most of the towns of
the state had come on the road map, but still there was no
mention of village link roads in the state.

The accessibility to rural areas greatly increased by 1970
(Fig. 17). There are a very few villages along the borders of the
state which by that time remained beyond a distance of 6.4
kilometres from a metalled road. This increase in accessibility to
roads has been accelerated with the construction of village
roads. By the end of 1969, the road length in Punjab reached
9,960 kilometres and two-thirds of the villages and an equal
proportion of the rural population had either come on metalled
roads or were within 1.6 kilometres of them. The villages beyond
eight kilometres from the roads are hardly one per cent of
the total inhabited villages of the state.

Table 49

Rural accessibility to roads, 1969

Detail	Total	Within 1.6 km.	1.6-3.2 km.	3.2-4.8 km.	4.8-6.4 km.	6.4-8 km.	Beyond 8 km.
Inhabited villages	11,947	7,866 (65.84%)	2,670 (22.35%)	973 (8.17%)	297 (0.98%)	116 (0 98%)	25 (0.20%)
Rural population	8,567,763	5,698,417 (66.50%)	1,850,555 (21.59%)	690,264 (8.05%)	214,536 (2.50%)	91,545 (1 06%)	22,546 (0.14%)

Source: Mavi, *Roads in the Rural Punjab*, P.A.U., 1970.

Intensity of Roads. The length of roads in Punjab in terms of
per unit area and population is now comparable with the all-India
average and other states of India. However, as Table 50 shows,

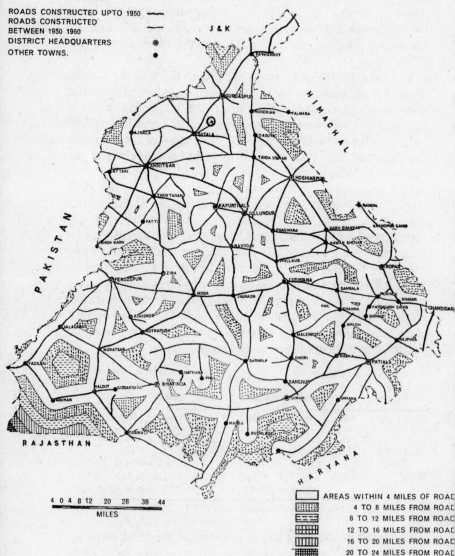

Fig. 16 Punjab—accessibility to roads, 1960

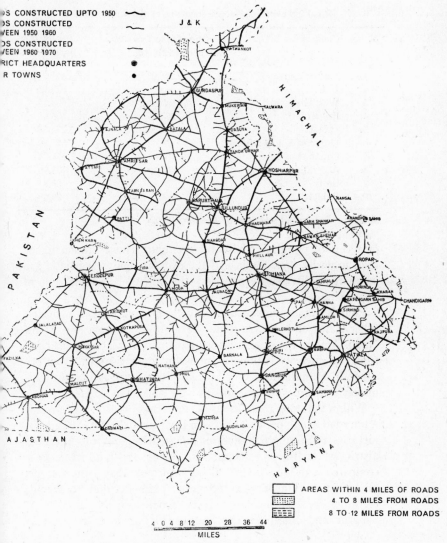

PUNJAB
CESSIBILITY TO ROADS
1970

)S CONSTRUCTED UPTO 1950
)S CONSTRUCTED
VEEN 1950 1960
)S CONSTRUCTED
VEEN 1960 1970
RICT HEADQUARTERS
R TOWNS

J & K

HIMACHAL

PAKISTAN

RAJASTHAN

HARYANA

PATHANKOT
GURDASPUR
MUKERIAN
TALWARA
TANDA URMAR
BATALA
DASUYA
AJNALA
AMRITSAR
HOSHIARPUR
ATTARI
TARN TARAN
KAPURTHALA
JULLUNDUR
NANGAL
ANANDPUR SAHIB
PATTI
PHAGWARA
GARH SHANKAR
NAWAN SHEHAR
HEM KARN
NAKODAR
ROPAR
ZIRA
PHILLAUR
LUDHIANA
FEROZEPUR
SAMRALA
MORINDA
KHARAR
MOGA
JAGRAON
CHANDIGARH
FAZILKA SENGARH SAHIB
JALALABAD
FARIDKOT
KHANNA
PAL
SIRHIND
AMLOH
KOTKAPURA
MALERKOTLA
RAJPURA
MUKATSAR
NABHA
BARNALA
PATIALA
NATHANA
GHURI
ABOHAR
MALOUT
BHATINDA
PHUL
SANGRUR
SAMANA
SUNAM
DABWALI
MANSA
BUDHLADA

AREAS WITHIN 4 MILES OF ROADS
4 TO 8 MILES FROM ROADS
8 TO 12 MILES FROM ROADS

4 0 4 8 12   20   28   36   44
MILES

Fig. 17   Punjab—accessibility to roads, 1970

road intensity in Punjab stands nowhere in comparison with countries of north-western Europe.

Table 50

Road intensity in selected countries of the world, 1967

S.No.	Country	Road length in kms. per 256 sq. km.	Per '00,000 population
1.	Netherlands	506.08	527.74
2.	U.K.	365.92	629.92
3.	West Germany	360.64	603.15
4.	France	352.16	1,505.85
5.	U.S.A.	123.52	2,272.68
6.	Union of South Africa	24.48	623.89
7.	Canada	14.24	2,744.86
8.	Australia	12.00	3,103.96
9.	India	25.12	68.8
10.	Punjab	51.2	89.6

Source: *Statistical Abstract of Punjab*, 1969.

In terms of population also those countries have a much higher road intensity than Punjab. If the average figures for India are compared with these countries the picture becomes more depressing.

Punjab stands conspicuously high in comparison with the other states of India. It comes next only to Kerala and Tamil Nadu. Among the states of northern India, Punjab stands at the top. The intensity is almost double in comparison with Andhra Pradesh, Maharashtra, Gujarat and Uttar Pradesh and approximately four times in comparison with Rajasthan.

Within the state, road intensity varies a good deal. The maximum road length per unit area is in Ludhiana where it is 67.2 kilometres per 256 square kilometres and the minimum is in Bhatinda district where it is 36.8 kilometres. When this road intensity is compared with that of 1950, it becomes clear that in the districts of Amritsar, Gurdaspur, Jullundur, Ludhiana and Ferozepur, the intensity has increased three times. In the districts of Sangrur and Bhatinda this increase is more than five-fold (Table 52).

In terms of population the intensity is maximum in Patiala

Table 51
Road intensity in the states of India, 1969

S. No.	State	Road length in kms. per 256 sq. kms.	Per '00,000 population
1.	Kerala	128.46	97.21
2.	Tamil Nadu	79.62	108.12
3.	Punjab	51.20	89.60
4.	West Bengal	46.24	38.68
5.	Mysore	46.24	124.99
6.	Maharashtra	25.68	64.48
7.	Andhra Pradesh	25.68	63.48
8.	Uttar Pradesh	23.12	31.74
9.	Bihar	20.54	24.80
10.	Gujarat	20.54	59.52
11.	Madhya Pradesh	15.40	66.46
12.	Orissa	15.40	44.64
13.	Rajasthan	12.83	52.41
14.	Assam	10.27	35.71
	India	**25.12**	**68.8**

Table 52
Road intensity in Punjab

S. No.	District	Road length in kms. per 256 sq. kms.		
		1950	1960	1970
1.	Ludhiana	22.72	32.0	67.2
2.	Gurdaspur	19.84	35.2	65.67
3.	Jullundur	23.54	35 2	64.64
4.	Amritsar	20.80	35.2	62.88
5.	Patiala	16.48	30.4	59.68
6.	Kapurthala	24.16	33.6	59.20
7.	Ropar	19.20	28.8	58.08
8.	Hoshiarpur	9.84	20.8	44.96
9.	Sangrur	4.96	22.88	44.00
10.	Ferozepore	11.36	20.8	38.56
11.	Bhatinda	7.68	20.8	36.96
	Punjab	**10.88***	**24.8***	**51.2**

*Figures pertain to Punjab before reorganization.
Source: Unpublished records, Office of the Chief Engineer, B&R, Punjab.

district where it comes to about 112 kilometres and is minimum in Jullundur district where it is about 70.4 kilometres. For most of the other districts of the state, the intensity is over 80 kilometres for every 100,000 population.

Table 53
Road intensity in Punjab

S. No.	District	Road length in kms. per '00,000 of population		
		1950	1960	1970
1.	Patiala	44.32	54.4	111 68
2.	Kapurthala	52.64	64.0	108.64
3.	Ropar	42.56	36.8	99.84
4.	Ferozepore	34.88	51.2	93.60
5.	Bhatinda	26.24	52.8	94.88
6.	Gurdaspur	31.84	36.8	91.04
7.	Sangrur	13.92	48.0	90.88
8.	Ludhiana	36.0	41.6	88.16
9.	Amritsar	29.6	44.8	81.12
10.	Hoshiarpur	19.36	40.0	78.40
11.	Jullundur	29.76	36.8	70.24
	Punjab	32.16*	49.6*	89.60

*Figures pertain to Punjab before reorganization.
Source: Unpublished records, Office of the Chief Engineer, B&R Punjab.

Conclusions. During the execution of the first phases of the crash programme, villagers showed extraordinary interest in getting roads to their villages. As a result, the government feels morally bound to construct the roads to link every village. According to a recent estimate, 4,000 villages have so far been directly connected with roads and there are still 8,000 villages which anxiously wait to come on the road map. This anxiety is genuine because of the visible impact on the economic and social life of the villages which have been provided with link roads. Villages with stiff clayey soils, which used to remain cut off from the rest of the world during the rainy season, are no longer isolated. Similarly, in sandy areas the villages which were surrounded by loose sand during several months of the dry summer are relieved of this difficulty because an all-weather hard crust has been provided for their carts, tractors and bicycles. With the provision of roads to the villages, the number of vehicles has increased, higher education has become accessible, health services are being utilized, the village economic pattern is becoming diversified, land prices are increasing, the cropping pattern is becoming more profitable and the efficiency of the farmers has greatly improved. This extraordinary impact in such a short period has resulted in villages still beyond the reach of a metalled road making a demand for it.

To provide a road link to every village is, however, not an easy task. At present there are about 8,000 villages which are to be provided with link roads. For this provision an estimated 12,800 kilometres of roads are to be constructed. Assuming that the land will be available free of cost and the earth work will be done by villagers, these single lane village roads will cost approximately Rs 50 crores. This is a huge amount but it has to be found. The day should not be far when every Punjab village is linked with a metalled road and there is a balance between the economic, cultural and social development of villages and towns. With road links, small holdings will become economic units. Villages will attract talent, finance and farm produce processing units. Rural Punjab will then come into the mainstream of our national development.

20. Impact of New Technology on System of Land Tenure and Human Labour Employment in Punjab

As only three or four years have passed since the development of high-yielding varieties and hybrids and their adoption, it will be some time before we know the result of the impact of new technology on the land tenure system and the pattern of human labour employment. Here an attempt is made to describe what direction these changes are taking. More specifically, the objectives are (i) to examine the recent shifts in land tenures in Punjab; and (ii) to examine the trends in employment and wage levels in the farm sector.

Sampling Design. The sampling design of the "cost of cultivation studies" of the Directorate of Economics and Statistics, Ministry of Food and Agriculture, for the Punjab State was followed for the purpose of random selection of 16 villages and holdings in various farm size groups. Following the survey method, the data were collected for three years—1967-68 through 1969-70. The study sample consisted of 109 owner cultivators, 49 owner-cum-tenant cultivators and two landless tenant cultivators. The findings of other studies are also used in the discussion on various items.

Land Tenure System. It will be seen from Table 69 that the sample contained only 1.24 per cent of tenant cultivators, 30.6 per cent owner-cum-tenant and no less than 68 per cent owner cultivators. This is supported by our recent Farm Management Studies in Ferozepore district (1968-69) according to which tenant cultivators, owner-cum-tenant cultivators and owner cultivators formed 0.67 per cent, 35.33 per cent and 64 per cent of the total number of holdings in the sample respectively (Table 69).

In the same study it was found (Table 54) that the ownership form was dominant and about 88.32 per cent area was self-cultivated. Perhaps the major problem of tenancy is only of crop sharing arrangements which covered 6.64 per cent of the total cultivated area in 1969-70.

Table 54

Percentage distribution of area in different tenures on the selected holdings, 1968-69 (district Ferozepore)

Year	Self-cultivated	Share rented	Cash rented	Total
1954-55	63.00	33.00	4.00	100
1967-68	89.73	7.10	3.17	100
1968-69	89.17	6.72	4.11	100
1969-70	88.32	6.64	5.04	100

Table 54 shows that the area under self-cultivation increased from 63 per cent in 1954-55 to 88.32 per cent in 1969-70. The area under cash rented land increased from four per cent in 1954-55 to 5.04 per cent in 1969-70 and that of share rented land decreased from 33 to 6.64 per cent in the corresponding period. This shows that even the practice of crop sharing is on the decline.

The break-up of leased area (Table 55) shows that the proportion of cash rented land to total leased land increased from 30.8 per cent in 1967-68 to 43.2 per cent in 1969-70 in Ferozepore district whereas share rented land declined from 69.2 to 56.8 per cent in the corresponding period.

This clearly supports our hypothesis that with the rise in the yield per hectare and the prices of farm products the proportion of cash rented land to share rented land tends to increase.

Sharing of Inputs. Before the introduction of new farm technology,

Table 55
Percentage break-up of leased-in area

	1967-68	1968-69	1969-70
Cash rented	30.8	37.9	43.2
Share rented	69.2	62.1	56.8
Total	**100.00**	**100.00**	**100.00**

the owner of the land did not share any costs with the tenants, with
the result that productivity per unit of land on share rented land
was normally low. It was felt that to induce the tenants to make
intensive use of modern technological inputs, the owner of the
land should share the cost of modern inputs used by tenants.
Examination of Table 56 shows that the owners shared about
50 per cent cost of new seeds, fertilizers and irrigation charges.

Table 56
Share of input cost between landlord and tenant 1967-68 through 1969-70 (expressed in per cent)

	Seed		Fertilizers		Irrigation		Others	
	Owner	Tenant	Owner	Tenant	Owner	Tenant	Owner	Tenant
1967-68	48	52	50	50	40	60	12	88
1968-69	49	51	50	50	42	58	8	92
1969-70	50	50	50	50	42	58	8	92

Operational Size of Holdings. It was hypothesized that, because
of partial modernization of agriculture and adoption of new
farm technology, small farmers should make their units of
cultivation more viable by leasing in more land and leasing
out less. This aspect is examined in Table 57.

Table 57
Distribution of percentage of leased-in area to total cultivated area on owned-cum-tenanted farms for various size groups in Punjab State, 1969-70

Holding size groups (acres)	Percentage of leased-in area to total cultivated area	Percentage of leased-out area to total cultivated area
Up to 9.5	24.6	nil
9.6 to 14.6	24.5	0.46
14.7 to 19.5	10.5	2.85
19.6 to 29.0	8.8	2.13
above 29.9	2.6	4.02

Table 57 shows a definite increase in the proportion of leased-in area to the total cultivated area from 2.6 per cent in the largest sized group of holdings to 24.6 per cent on the smallest sized group of holdings, whereas the percentage of leased-out area increased from 0.46 per cent in the small group to 4.02 per cent in the large holdings. This finding was also supported by the data of Farm Management Studies in Ferozepore district as shown in Table 58.

Table 58

Distribution of percentage of leased-in area to total cultivated area on owned-cum-tenanted farms for various size groups, Ferozepore district, 1968-69

Holding size group (hectares)	Percentage of leased-in area to total cultivated area	Percentage of leased-out area to total cultivated area
Below 6	23.0	4.28
6 to 9	27.1	4.50
9 to 14	36.1	4.33
14 to 24	34.1	5.51
24 and above	14.1	12.69

Land Transactions. Table 59 showing purchases, sales and land mortgages in and out indicates that land purchases were a common phenomenon in all size groups (7.14 per cent) and the lowest in the largest size group (4.76 per cent). The percentage of area added through purchases varied from 0.46 per cent in the largest size group to 2.85 per cent in the smallest size group of farms. This trend was reversed in respect of sales where the percentage of farmers selling land showed a tendency to increase with an increase in the farm size. The percentage of farmers who sold land was the highest (23.80 per cent) on the large farms and the lowest (7.14 per cent) in the small sized groups. The percentage of farmers who added land through mortgaging was higher on small farms than on large farms.

As a result of all these transactions over the three year period, on an average, the farmers in the smallest size groups (below 9.5 acres) made 0.95 per cent net increase in area over the area held at the beginning of the period, whereas the farmers in the largest size group (above 29 acres) had a net decrease of 2.5

Table 59

Purchase, sale and mortgage of land in various size groups, 1967-68 through 1969-70

Acres	Total No. of farmers in each group 1967-68	Purchase		Sale		Mortgaged-in		Mortgaged-out		Net increase or decrease over three years	
		%age of farmers purchasing total	%age of area purchased to total area owned	%age of farmers who sold	%age of area sold to total owned area	%age of no. of farmers who mortgaged-in	%age of area mortgaged-in to total area	%age of farmers who mortgaged-out	%age of area mortgaged-out to total area	Area (Acre)	%age
Up to 9.5	28	7.14	2.85	7.14	4.35	7.14	2.44	—	—	+0.07	0.95
9.6 to 14.6	17	5.88	0.52	—	—	17.65	3.52	—	—	+0.47	4.03
14.7 to 19.5	16	6.25	0.70	12.5	0.70	—	—	—	—	—	—
19.6 to 29.0	27	4.81	0.29	—	—	—	—	11.11	2.25	−0.26	−1.0
Above 29	21	4.76	0.46	23.80	3.25	4.76	2.81	—	—	−1.25	−2.5

per cent in their respective areas.

Rental Value. Due to the adoption of new farm technology and particularly of high-yielding varieties and installation of tube-wells, the rental value of land experienced a steep rise as shown in Table 60. The table indicates that in case of irrigated lands, the rental value per acre increased from Rs 302.50 in 1967-68 to Rs 418.50 in 1969-70. In case of unirrigated lands the corresponding increase for the same period was from Rs 190 to Rs 245.35 per acre.

Table 60

Impact of new technology on the rate of rent per acre, 1967-68 to 1969-70 (Punjab)

	1967-68	1968-69		1969-70	
		in Rs	Percentage increase over 1967-68	in Rs	Percentage increase over 1967-68
Irrigated	302.50	408.39	35.00	418.50	38.34
Unirrigated	190.00	233.00	22.63	245.35	29.13

This trend of rising rental value of land is supported by the findings of Farm Management Studies in Ferozepore district where land rent per hectare increased from Rs 475 in 1967-68 to Rs 556 in 1968-69.

Pattern of Employment of Labour. The question is often raised that mechanization of agriculture might displace farm labour. The answer to this question would largely depend upon the stage of economic development and pattern of mechanization followed in agriculture. Even if we follow a theoretical model, substitution of capital for labour should take place at a far distant point on the expansion path of the agricultural sector in India.

In fact, the present stage of farm technology and pattern of mechanization followed in Punjab have resulted in increased employment of human labour due to increases in cropping intensity and increased production per unit of time and area.

A study of nine demonstration farms in Jullundur district

Table 61

Changes in farm labour, bullocks and tractor use in Punjab based on a sample of progressive farms in Punjab*

Year	Average acreage		Intensity of cropping	Total labour used (M. Hours)	Labour used per cropped acre (M. Hours)	per culti-vated acre	Bullock hours used per cropped acre	Tractor hours used per cropped acre
	Cultivated	Cropped						
1966-67	33.19	42.05	126.69	11,481	273	346	127.53	11.94
1967-68	33.87	44.73	132.06	13,821	309	408	76.15	9.58
1968-69	36.85	49.89	135.39	16,310	327	443	48.4	12.72
1969-70	36.78	53.06	144.26	18,145	336	494	35.66	17.24

*From the files of the Department of Economics and Sociology, Punjab Agricultural University, Ludhiana.

Source: Nine Demonstration Centres in Jullundur district.

gave an indication that the additional horse power provided through tractors and tube-wells made it possible to increase cropping intensity from 126.69 per cent in 1966-67 to 144.26 per cent in 1969-70. The use of human labour on the farm increased by 58 per cent over this period. Only bullock labour use was reduced from 127.53 hours in 1966-67 to 35.66 hours in 1969-70 (Table 61).

These findings are supported by the Farm Management Studies in Ferozepore district (1968-69). According to Table 62, human labour employment per cropped hectare increased from 51 days in 1954-55 through 1956-57 to 59.73 days in 1968-69. But bullock labour employment was reduced from nine days per hectare of cultivated area on mechanized holdings against 21 days on bullock operated holdings. Thus, substitution of machinery took place not for human labour but for bullock labour, which is a highly desirable development because it saves land put under fodder to feed bullocks.

Because of the complementarity between labour and capital in the context of present technological developments, and emphasis on multiple cropping and increased productivity per unit of time and area, the production function should continue to be labour-intensive for many years to come.

Table 62

Employment of human labour per hectare of cropped area, 1967-68 and 1968-69 (Ferozepore district)

Year	Family exchange	Hired labour	Total human labour
1954-55 through 1955-57	37.30	13.78	51.08
1967-68	28.86	28.19	57.05
1968-69	30.27	29.46	59.73

Again, the present pattern of farm technology has increased labour employment in terms of number of days worked during the year which is clear from Table 63.

It is apparent from Table 63 that annual labour input increased from 277.57 days in 1967-68 to 322.82 days in 1969-70.

Table 63

Total annual inputs of labour by a family worker and permanent farm servants (Ferozepore district)

Year	Family farm worker permanent farm servant
1967-68	277.57
1968-69	293.27
1969-70	322.82

The extent of employment of human labour was also studied with regard to its employment on different combinations of power on the farm on the basis of per unit of cropped area as shown in Table 64.

Table 64

Employment of human labour per hectare of cropped area on different combinations of power, 1968-69, Ferozepore district

Size group (hectares)	Tube-well operated holding		Canal irrigated holding	
	Tractor operated	Bullock operated	Tractor operated	Bullock operated
Below 6	—	72.23	—	61.76
6 to 9	61.47	71.93	—	51.35
9 to 14	76.69	78.83	60.22	63.68
14 to 24	57.33	53.30	—	46.06
24 and above	39.45	—	45.53	47.76
Average per cropped hectare	58.79	69.08	52.88	52 12
Average per cultivated hectare	92.50	96.13	51.13	57.04

Table 64 shows that with the present pattern of farm mechanization, employment of human labour did not decrease in tractor operated farms under canal irrigated areas. In tube-well irrigated areas, human labour employment per cropped hectare was 59 days in tractorized holdings against 69 days on bullock operated holdings. But in case of cultivated area, 92.50 labour days were used in tractor operated holdings against 96.13 days on bullock operated holdings. It could be concluded from these studies that if at all farm mechanization replaced some unskilled labour per cropped hectare, it was more than compensated for by increased intensity of cropping and labour-intensive operations such as interculture, irrigation, manuring, fertilizing and harvesting. Owing to the divisible nature of a part of farm technology such as high-yielding varieties and hybrids, and intensive use of fertilizers and irrigation which could be utilized even by small farmers, and other complementary changes released in the process, various forms of capital seemed to have acted as complementary forces of human labour rather than causing its displacement. Punjab has definitely been experiencing a labour shortage at peak periods because of increased intensity of cropping. Even on the experimental farm areas of the Punjab Agricultural University's Ludhiana campus, of the total permanent labour employed, 48 per cent came from outside Punjab and of the casual hired labour employed on the farm, 56 per cent belonged to other states.

Wage Rates. At the state level, changes in farm workers' wage rates were examined. According to *Statistical Abstract, Punjab*, wages increased by 61, 64, and 90 per cent each for ploughing, sowing, hoeing and harvesting operations respectively. The wage of skilled workers such as carpenters and blacksmiths rose by 66 and 68 per cent respectively during this period. The rise in farm wages is borne out by Table 65.

Table 65

Impact of technology on wage rate per day per casual labour,
1967-68 through 1969-70 (Punjab)

	1967-68	*1968-69*		*1969-70*	
	In rupees	*In rupees*	*Percentage increase over 1967-68*	*In rupees*	*Percentage increase over 1967-68*
Ordinary period	3.75	4.90	30.66	5.50	46.66
Peak period (wheat crop)	6.00	8.60	43.33	9.50	58.33
Percentage increase over ordinary period	60%	75.51%		72.73%	

(Wage rate includes meals charges also)

The wages rose from Rs 3.75 per day per labourer in 1967-68 to Rs 5.50 in 1969-70, showing an increase of 46.66 per cent. In case of peak period, the rise was even higher—from six rupees in 1967-68 to Rs 9.50 in 1969-70, i.e., an increase of 58.33 per cent.

This trend is also supported by Farm Management Studies in Ferozepore district as will be seen from Table 66.

Table 66

Average daily wage of casual adult male field labourer, Ferozepore district

Year	Average wages per day in rupees
1967-68	5.55
1968-69	6.39
1969-70	6.67

Annual Payment to Permanent Farm Servants. The annual wages to permanent farm servants increased from Rs 1,029 in 1967-68 to Rs 1,286.50 in 1969-70 (Table 67).

Table 67

Annual wage to permanent labour in 1967-68 to 1969-70 in rupees (Punjab)

Size group	1967-68	1968-69	1969-70
A	1,065.00	1,205.00	1,313.00
B	985.00	1,069.00	1,188.00
C	1,045.50	1,130.00	1,313.00
D	1,025.50	1,138.00	1,346.50
E	1,050.50	224.00	1,370.00
Average	**1,029.00**	**1,138.00**	**1,286.50**

The total wage payments in case of permanent labour registered an increase in all the farm size groups. The rising trend of wages paid to annual farm servants was also supported by the finding of Farm Management Studies in Ferozepore district as shown in Table 68.

On an average, the annual wage rate per farm servant increased from Rs 1,520 in 1967-68 to Rs 1,877 in 1969-70.

Rising wage rates are direct indications of increasing demand

Table 68

Total wages paid to annual farm servant per annum on the selected holding, 1967-68 to 1969-70 (Ferozepore district)

Size groups (hectares)	1967-68	1968-69	1969-70
Below 6	1,051	1,561	1,723
6 to 9	1,631	1,308	1,704
9 to 14	1,856	1,609	1,846
14 to 24	1,892	1,705	2,067
24 and above	1,167	1,807	2,071
Average	**1,520**	**1,608**	**1,877**

for labour. In fact, the pressure of rising wages is compelling the Punjab farmer to look more and more to further mechanization of such operations as harvesting of crops. Through time, when such labour-consuming operations such as harvesting and levelling are fully mechanized, some substitution of capital for labour might take place. But meanwhile, newly established processing and manufacturing units in the agricultural sector should be able to provide more employment. For this purpose, development programmes should be streamlined to provide the necessary skills to farm workers to help them get gainful employment in the agricultural industry.

To summarize, the land ownership system dominates Punjab's agriculture and there is no serious problem of tenancy.

The small farmers leased in more land than they leased out to make their unit of cultivation at least somewhat viable.

Finding the intensive use of modern technological inputs profitable, land owners have started sharing the cost of new seeds, fertilizers and irrigation charges with the tenants.

At the present stage of farm technology, farm mechanization has resulted in increased employment of human labour owing to the increase in cropping intensity. Thus, farm machinery did not displace human labour but bullock labour, which is a desirable development.

Farm wage rates are rising fast in Punjab. The pressure of rising wages is compelling the farmer to adopt mechanization of such operations as threshing and harvesting of crops.

Table 69

Distribution of number of holdings according to tenure system in various farm size groups, 1969-70

Farm size groups (acres)	Owner cultivators		Owner-cum-Tenant cultivators		Tenant cultivators		Total cultivators	
	No. of holdings	Percentage	No. of holdings	Percentage	No. of holdings	Percentage	No. of holdings	Percentage
Up to 9.5	28	77.77	8	22.23	—	—	36	100
9.6 to 14.6	17	53.13	15	46.87	—	—	32	100
14.7 to 19.5	16	59.26	9	33.33	2	7.41	27	100
19.6 to 29.0	27	77.14	8	22.86	—	—	35	100
29.0 and above	21	70.00	9	30.00	—	—	30	100
Total	109	68.13	49	39.63	2	1.24	160	100

Table 70

Distribution of number of holdings according to tenure system in Ferozepore district, 1968-69

Holding size groups (hectares)	Owner cultivators		Owner-cum-tenant cultivators		Tenant cultivators		Total	
	No. of holdings	Percentage to total no. of farms	No. of holdings	Percentage to total no. of farms	No. of holdings	Percentage to total no. of farms	No. of holdings	Percentage
Below 6	27	77.14	8	22.86	—	—	35	100
6-9	17	60.71	11	39.29	—	—	28	100
9-14	21	55.26	17	44.74	—	—	38	100
14-24	23	60.53	14	36.84	1	2.63	38	100
24 and above	8	72.73	3	27.27	—	—	11	100
Total	96	64.00	53	35.33	1	0.67	150	100

21. Impact of the Green Revolution on Punjab

The improved varieties which were available before the Green Revolution were only marginally superior to the varieties cultivated by the farmers whereas the new wheats provide a sharp contrast by doubling or even trebling the crop yield. The impact which these Mexican varieties have made on wheat production is startling. In 1961-62, the production of wheat in Punjab was 1,763,000 tonnes. In 1971-72, it was about 5,600,000 tonnes. Today Punjab is producing one-fourth of the total grain requirement of the whole country. This is a real technological breakthrough, for it is for the first time that man has acquired control over the vagaries of rainfall in this region.

I have earlier referred to the role of the human element in agriculture. Punjab is different from other states of India, as the villagers are more educated. There are about half a million serving soldiers and pensioners in the countryside. Apart from these there are large numbers of schoolteachers, minor government officials, policemen, and truck, taxi and lorry drivers who have roots in the countryside. All these skilled men have played a productive role in agriculture. They have invested their savings in land development, and have also intelligence and education to grasp the intricacies of tractors, machines and plant-protection chemicals. In fact, the best agriculture is practised by families some of whose members are educated. Among the totally illiterate, agriculture is poorest.

The social side effects of the Green Revolution have not been entirely beneficial in countries like Pakistan and Mexico where the system of land ownership is such that there is wide disparity in size of holdings, with most people working on small holdings and a few people in possession of the vast expanse of land. While the owners of large farms have unduly prospered, the condition of the peasantry has not perceptibly improved. In Mexico the real income of landless labourer decreased from $68 in 1950 to $56 in 1960. In Pakistan the wages of landless labourers remained static.

On the other hand, in Indian Punjab, there is an equitable system of land distribution and as a result the benefits of the Green Revolution have reached a large mass of people. With the implementation of current land reforms the base of the social pyramid will further broaden.

The Green Revolution in Punjab has benefited all farmers, big, medium and small. A cliche, often repeated by theoreticians, is that only big farmers have benefited from the Green Revolution. This is untrue. The success of a farmer in adopting new technology depends upon his luck in finding adequate ground water. Even small farmers with holdings of two to five hectares who have been able to bore successful tube-wells have adopted the new technology. The Green Revolution has benefited not only the farmers, but also farm labourers who command high wages in cash and are also fed by the farmers. In fact, their wages have more than doubled.

The phenomenal increase in production of foodgrains has not only saved the country from a grave political crisis but also provided stimulus to the economy. There is now less talk of recession in the industrial sector. A large demand for consumer goods has arisen. Industries which manufacture bicycles, sewing machines, watches, transistor radios and textiles have benefited a great deal from the agricultural revolution. The stagnant economy of towns has received a stimulus. Many new markets for sale of foodgrains have developed. They have adequate arrangements for storage of surplus foodgrains and large numbers of newly built shops. The shops are brighter and have more goods to sell. The number of shops selling agricultural chemicals, machinery and implements, and textiles, have noticeably increased. Repair shops for tractors, diesel engines and pump-sets have multiplied. The requirements of the new agriculture, in terms of fertilizers, plant-protection chemicals, pump-sets, electric motors, pipe sprayers and dusters are tremendous.

The intensive cultivation of Mexican wheats taught the use of fertilizers to the farmers. Having learnt this new technology, they are applying it to other crops like sugarcane, cotton, oilseeds, fruits and vegetables.

Increased grain production has given a stimulus to poultry farming. Small and large poultry farms have grown all over the state. Poultry and eggs are being consumed in larger quantities. People whose diet was mostly vegetarian now consume a protein-rich diet. Besides, the quantity of manure available for crop-raising has greatly increased.

It is for the first time that time has acquired value for the Indian farmers. With the ready availability of water all year round from tube-wells, double or even triple cropping has become a common practice.

Intensive farming with the new technology has generated demand for more farm labour. As a result, acute labour shortage has arisen. Another contributory cause is that sons of Harijans, who are landless labourers, after receiving education, are going into professions and skilled jobs and are no longer interested in working on farms as unskilled labourers. The gap in labour supply is being partially filled by migrant labour from overpopulated eastern Uttar Pradesh and the dry areas of Rajasthan.

Agriculture had remained stagnant in countries like India because the producers never got remunerative prices for their crops because government policies were consumer-oriented. Another tragedy of these countries was that the administrative services were overloaded with officials who had no experience of agriculture and rural life. Most of them were from urban castes and classes who were the traditional exploiters of the agriculturists. Hence it was too much to expect that they would view their problems with sympathy. This has been the bane of Indian agriculture. A radical departure came in 1966 on account of the compulsion of food shortages when the Government of India adopted the policy of giving remunerative prices for foodgrains. It paid rich dividends in increased food production as well as in the stimulus it provided to the economy.

In the strategy of transforming traditional agriculture into modernized agriculture, incentives to guide and reward farmers are a critical component. "Once there are investment opportunities and efficient incentives, farmers will turn sand into gold,"* observes Schultz. Of the incentives, price support is the best. We have seen its beneficial effect on Punjab agriculture. In many districts in Punjab the farmers have levelled sand dunes and have installed tube-wells. Thus they have literally turned sand into gold and have started productive agriculture on lands regarded as useless.

The price support policy for wheat adopted by the Government of India is a key factor which has assured the success of the Wheat Revolution. Not only is the price offered remunerative but arrangements are also made to purchase the foodgrains through the Food Corporation of India and the State Marketing Federation. Thus the strategy of grain dealers, who used to join together to depress the price at the time of harvest when the farmers sell, and raise it a few months later when there was acute consumer demand, was defeated. The impact of this policy can be judged from the fact that the wheat acreage in the country which was 12.8 million hectares in 1966-67 rose to 15.8 million hectares in 1969-70 and production rose from 11.3 million tonnes to 20.4 million tonnes. The average yield per hectare rose from 887 kilos to 1,263 kilos. It was for the first time that the empty granaries of India filled up, and we were emancipated from dependence on PL-480 supplies. The pivot of the programme is remunerative price for the farmers. So long as the farmers get a remunerative price for their production which enables them to meet the cost of inputs like fertilizers, plant-protection chemicals, quality seed, charges for family as well as hired labour, bills for electricity and diesel oil, depreciation of agricultural machinery, and also make a reasonable profit, they will continue to invest and the agricultural revolution will roll along bringing still larger areas under its sweep. However, the temptation of whittling down the profit of the farmers should be resisted so that their enthusiasm is not killed. The requirements of modern

*Theodore W. Schultz, *Transforming Traditional Agriculture*, first Indian edition, 1970, p. 5.

agriculture in terms of resources are tremendous. The farmers have been ploughing back their profits in land improvement, sinking of tube-wells, installing underground systems of irrigation, purchase of tractors, pumping sets, sprayers and costly implements. Let this process go on for a number of years and we will notice the liquidation of rural slums over vast areas in India, and a firm foundation will have been laid for development in other sectors of the economy.

The standard of living of farmers is still miserably low. There is much to be done to improve their education, housing and general living conditions. Their housing is wretched and furniture is practically non-existent in their homes. Their cattle sheds and tube-well structures should be vastly improved. Each farmer requires more space for storage of grain. The only solid achievement of the agricultural change is that the farmers and their labourers eat better, they have provided food to the city dwellers of India, and they have liberated the country from its dependence on foreign countries for their daily bread. They have also demonstrated that traditional agriculture can be modernized in a short period and that the situation in India is not hopeless as some people imagined. Besides, they have earned a breathing spell of a few years against the torrent of rising population during which the family planning programme should be effectively implemented.

22. Profile of a Village—Shahpur

Socio-economic surveys in Punjab's villages have stressed how farmers have doubled their annual incomes and women are no longer dependants but equal partners in their homes. But these surveys do not tell the story of how slummy clusters of mud huts are being turned into semi-urban townships— a story as exciting as that of the agricultural breakthrough.

A sample village, such as Shahpur, about 29 kilometres from Ludhiana off the Delhi-Amritsar Grand Trunk Road, shows how development is changing the lives of villagers. The road leading to it branches off the highway at Doraha, about 22 kilometres from Ludhiana, and a 6.4 kilometre drive brings one to this secluded community, with a separate, independent life of its own.

Once part of the princely state of Patiala, Shahpur was included in Patiala district when Pepsu was formed. In 1962 it was brought under Ludhiana district. The village is believed to have been founded by four families about 150 to 200 years ago. The members of these families, who lived in the nearby village of Kaddon, are said to have quarrelled with their Harijan neighbours and quit their ancestral homes. As the area where Shahpur stands was a jungle, the four families cleared part of it and settled down there.

The new village was named Shahpur either because the settlers were *shahs* (money-lenders) or after a recluse known as Shadhya, who had made the jungle his home. Whatever the reason, the links between Kaddon and Shahpur are still maintained and there are common sub-castes in the two villages. Almost all

Shahpurians make it a point to attend a religious mela in Kaddon, held every year around Divali.

Though a predominantly Jat Sikh village, its population includes people of other castes and some Muslims. The Muslim villagers were in fact carefully protected during the partition riots in 1947. They were neither allowed to leave nor exposed to danger. They were made to hide in Sikh homes until the killings were over.

The Muslims might have been saved only partly on humanitarian grounds. The main reason possibly was that they were needed to perform essential, age-old functions which others could not be expected to do. It is not clear whether the Sikhs wanted to keep the social structure intact or spare themselves the effort of finding substitutes for people who have been, and to this day are, what may be described as the retainers of the entire village community.

The Muslim residents include two families of *telis* (oil crushers), six families of potters, one family each of Mirasis, drummers and weavers, and some Gujjars. The drummer is the village counterpart of the town crier. He makes public announcements. For instance, when pits and pot-holes in a kucha road have to be filled by *shramdan*, he goes round beating his drum and letting everyone know where and when they have to work. The Mirasi is the common village messenger and his wife presides over *siapas*—breast-beating mourning sessions after a death. The Gujjars have the function of protecting village crops against stray cattle, maintaining common stud bulls for cows and taking the village cattle to graze. The weaver produces *khes* and coarse cloth for sacking.

All these people are given payment in the form of grain after every harvest. Each farming family deals with them directly and pays them separately except in the case of Gujjars who, in addition to receiving their share of grain along with the others, enjoy free grazing rights for their own cattle.

The village tailors—three families—are Sikhs who, instead of being paid in kind, are paid in cash. Their business is slumping as the villagers with their changing modes of dress have begun to patronize tailors in urban areas.

There are three families of Brahmins who, while continuing

their priestly calling, own small grocery shops.   Brahmin priests
are still in demand because the Jat Sikhs of Shahpur generally
observe a mixture of Hindu and Sikh rites.

The only goldsmith in the village is a Sikh in appearance but
has a Hindu name.   With not many customers coming to him
as a goldsmith, he also runs a grocery shop.

There are two families of Bairagis.   They are somewhat akin
to sadhus.   They have Hindu names like Darshan Das and
Gurdas but have long hair and beards like Sikhs.   Their
profession is begging.

The Scheduled castes, all Sikhs, live in a segregated part of
the village.   The 30 or so Harijan families had houses in the
original village itself, but some years ago it was decided by
common consent that they should be provided with land to build
their own settlement on the outskirts of the village.   They were
given more land for housing than that they had vacated, for
they were in no sense ejected but merely asked to move a little
away so that they could carry on their specialized trades like the
skinning of dead animals and tanning, without filling the whole
village with malodorous smells.

Today the Harijan quarter of the village has paved streets.
About 70 per cent of the houses are pucca and about 50 per cent
of them have independent electricity connections.

The Harijans count among them one barber, two *jheurs,* two
sweepers and a number of cobblers, carpenters and blacksmiths.
The barber may be called upon to cook for any farmer's family
entertaining a large number of guests, as the villagers do not
observe caste taboos like untouchability.   The barber's wife has
a more important role.   After a girl's wedding in the village, it
is she who accompanies the bride when she goes to her in-laws'
home for the first time.

The *jheurs* clean utensils at weddings and on other festive
occasions.   As for the sweepers, the job of one is to keep the
village streets clean by removing cowdung and other refuse,
while the other works in the houses. Of the cobblers, nowadays
only the older generation makes and repairs shoes.   Members
of the younger generation, who have had the benefit of an
education, look for office jobs or hope to become teachers in
basic schools after their training.   Quite a few young Harijans

of the village are already teaching in schools. Those not so lucky work as farm labourers.

Harijan women breed cattle. They rear both cows and buffaloes and sell them. To supplement their incomes they glean the fields after the wheat and groundnut crops have been harvested. Since farmers do not want to waste their time and labour in picking what is embedded in the soil, these women and their children collect the leavings—grains of wheat and groundnut pods—as their own share. After a good groundnut harvest a woman can make up to ten rupees a day during the season which lasts for about a month.

The carpenters and blacksmiths make and repair old fashioned agricultural implements in return for seasonal payment in kind.

The four score or so Jat Sikh families of Shahpur depend mainly on farming. However, the men, from about a quarter of these families, have joined the army. A very small number are truck owners or drivers in Calcutta. They start as drivers, save some money and buy a truck in partnership with others. Those who make good buy their own trucks.

The total amount of land owned by the village, including fields, houses, ponds and roads, is 540 acres. As the holdings are rather small, some villagers have bought 250 acres of land in neighbouring areas. In one instance, ten Shahpur families bought a whole village in the Rajpura block, renamed it Shahpur and settled down there.

Though Shahpur is a medium sized village with no large holdings, it is not only progressive but prosperous too, and its people enjoy a fairly high standard of living. The village has over a dozen tractors and about 100 tube-wells. Its cooperative, with about 260 members, has recently built an imposing godown at a cost of over Rs 25,000 to store fertilizers, insecticides and pesticides.

As for living conditions, all but five per cent, of the houses are pucka and many of them are double storeyed. Almost all of them have electricity connections. For drinking water each house has its own hand-pump, and some have more than one. The streets are paved and are kept reasonably clean. About 70 per cent of the homes have radio sets—not transistor sets which for some reason are not popular.

Another proof of Shahpur's prosperity is that more than 30 people in the village own rifles. They are bought ostensibly for shikar but are actually meant for self-protection. Since there are long-standing family feuds some people do not feel secure unless they carry a rifle of their own when challenged by a rifle bearing opponent. A few years ago, two persons were killed in one of these armed encounters.

Educationally, the village is fairly progressive. Though there is only a primary school in the village, there are a number of matriculates. Shahpur boasts half a dozen graduates and at least two postgraduates. There are also a number of girls who have done their matriculation, apart from those who have passed their middle school examination. Thanks to a sewing centre run by the community development set-up, almost all the girls can stitch their clothes at home.

While drinking and meat eating are fairly widespread in Punjab, the people of Shahpur do so only on festive occasions. One of the restrictive factors may be that there are no liquor or meat shops in rural areas, but it appears that the real reason, particularly where drinking is concerned, is the hold of tradition. Drinking as a habit is not approved of, but there are no taboos on drinking occasionally. As to meat eating, few farmers would care to kill a sheep or a goat for a family meal. Their vegetarian fare is so satisfying that they do not appear to have any desire for meat.

If opium eating can be said to be prevalent in the Punjab countryside, it is only among a very small, almost an insignificant group of people. Shahpur, for instance, has no more than three or four addicts.

But the tobacco habit is another story. Over 50 per cent of Harijan Sikhs of the village, it is believed, either smoke cigarettes or chew zarda (scented tobacco). The traditional hookah is seen only in the homes of a few Muslims of the older generation.

The younger men among the village farmers nowadays wear a kurta and tight pyjamas (not churidars) made of synthetic fabrics. They find them durable and easy-to-wash materials and the workmanlike trousers preferable to the unwieldy lungi-type cotton chaddar and kurta sported by the older generation. Educated young men who make up about 20 per cent of the population, wear western-style trousers. The turban, of course, is a must for all.

Talking of turbans, synthetic fabrics have driven the traditional dyer out of existence. These fabrics are available in so many textures and so many shades and colours that the dyer has become redundant. As women also wear the new fabrics, the dyer is no longer in demand. Women generally wear the *salwar-kameez*, but teenagers prefer a *kurta* and *churidars*, like girls in the cities.

The main kharif crops of the village are maize and groundnut while cotton, sugarcane and fodder are also grown on a smaller scale. In the rabi season, the main crop is wheat along with a little barley and fodder.

In the absence of a stable government in the state, panchayat elections have not been held for a long time and Shahpur's panchayat has not been very active. But an organization called the Naujawan Kisan Sabha formed by young progressive farmers has filled the gap. The sabha came into being in 1967 and has about 40 members who have paid an admission fee of five rupees each and pay a rupee a month as subscription. It is keenly interested in the villagers' welfare, arranges demonstrations, plays and film shows in cooperation with the district public relations department and the Punjab Agricultural University in Ludhiana, and runs a library. Besides having about 250 books in Punjabi, the library subscribes to Punjabi monthly magazines and a Punjabi daily.

The sabha, popularly known in the village as the "Club," arranges to transport people to kisan melas and similar functions by tractor trolleys. In the slack season it also arranges trips to Ludhiana or the other nearby town of Khanna to enable people to see cinema shows. The idea is to provide recreation and attract more members to the sabha. The sabha is opposed to drinking in public and to drug taking.

The village has a committee to look after the local gurdwara which employs a *granthi* and a *sewadar*. Birthdays of all the gurus and the first day of every month are observed with proper ceremony. The committee has a tube-well to provide water for cattle.

Though the formal house of worship is the gurdwara, the people of Shahpur also take part in ceremonies at a *samadhi* at Kaddon where one celebrant is a Brahmin and the other a Muslim Mirasi and where both sweets and goats are offered to seek a boon or in thanksgiving. In the village itself, snakes are worshipped on one day of the year and the goddess of small-pox propitiated on another. There are also ceremonies for ancestor worship.

Brahmins and Muslims also take part in weddings. When the groom's party leaves for the bride's house a Mirasi leads with a drum and a Brahmin priest accompanies it. The bridal party also visits a gurdwara as part of the ceremonial.

While the people of the village are taking to modern clothes and have begun to acquire sofas and chairs (which a new daughter-in-law usually brings as part of her dowry) for their homes, there have apparently been few spectacular social changes. The old traditions are fully maintained but with prosperity the habit of spending lavishly on food and drink on occasions like weddings and feasts has grown.

Another sign of the times is that the neem twig, used to clean teeth, is being replaced by the toothbrush and that brides and even some unmarried girls are allowed to use lipstick and other cosmetics.

The villagers while away what little leisure they have in gossip or in playing cards. With the Green Revolution their work has increased and with both dairy farming and poultry keeping becoming popular, men as well as women will have more to do than ever before, especially because farm labour is scarce. The shortage is so acute and the demand so great that many people from U.P. find it profitable to travel to areas in the heart of Punjab, not excluding the village of Shahpur, to work as daily wage earners.

23. Profile of a Village—Jodhan

The agricultural revolution in Ludhiana is growing into what can only be called a "rural revolution." New ideas are gnawing at the roots of tradition in almost every walk of village life. What is emerging is a new style of living. There is ample evidence to show that the Ludhiana farmer attaches great importance to housing and the education of his children. Among other things, this has resulted in a marked improvement in the number of secondary schools both for boys as well as for girls, and it is a foregone conclusion that these better educated girls will want a different way of life to that of their mothers. As in the cities so in the villages, they feel that it is they, and not their mothers-in-law, who should have a greater say in the preparation of domestic budgets and the bringing up of children. This trend is by no means confined to the better off farmers. It has also spread to non-agriculturists, who too have started earning more in the last few years and now look forward to a better all-round standard of living.

The farmers of Ludhiana already produce more wheat per hectare than their counterparts anywhere else in the world. In the ten years since it was started, the intensive agricultural development programme has increased the gross income of its 40,000 farm families from Rs 23 crores in 1961 to over Rs 70 crores this year.

With each new technique that he has adopted, the farmer's ideas have changed. He has learnt the importance of crop budgets and the combination of inputs, practices and crop rotations which will maximize his net income.

His new business outlook is reflected in the fact that he now reserves a part of his holding for seasonal vegetable crops. Five years ago this practice was unheard of. In 1965 the average Sikh Jat would have had nothing to do with growing *bhindis* and *tindas*. Regardless of its profitability, he then looked upon the raising of vegetable crops as an occupation strictly for the lower castes.

Not only are Ludhiana's 40,000 farmers and their families earning more, they are also spending more. In shaking off the old emphasis on thrift they have imparted a shock wave to the rest of the district's economy, opening up new opportunities for its remaining 1.2 million people.

Every big village in the district now has a new cluster of smartly painted and whitewashed shops. Many of them are virtually indistinguishable from those to be found in any small town. This is not all. Several of the larger villages now have more than one banking institution each. The new technology calls for heavy investments, and this in turn has created a new demand for credit-services.

In Jodhan, a village with 300 households on the Ludhiana-Pakhowal road, the two tailoring establishments stock over 250 different kinds of prints and plain shades each. They are good enough to be located on Janpath in New Delhi.

Five years ago, their owners used to ply their sewing machines themselves and stocked perhaps a dozen grades of fairly cheap cloth and little else. Each of them now supervises his own team of hired tailors who are kept fairly busy all year round.

The nearby provision stores in the village stock everything from nail polish to toothpaste. On a recent visit I counted two types of lipsticks, several brands of plastic shoes and leather sandals, four types of talcum powder, a wide choice of hair oils, laces, ribbons, toilet soaps, vaseline, plastic buckets, notebooks, pencils, batteries, torches, biscuits, combs, brushes, *agarbattis,* buttons and a brand each of bleaching powder and hair remover.

Equally enterprising are the numerous shops dealing in domestic electrical appliances and fittings. Ninety per cent of villages in the district are electrified, and there is a thriving trade in switches, plugs, bulb holders, adapters, plastic wiring, conduits, electric irons and table fans.

Another common sight is the inevitable "English wine and beer" shop. Liquor and prosperity in the Punjab countryside seem to go together. There has been a manifold increase in the state's revenues from excise and other taxes on the sale of alcohol. A great many of the elders are quick to decry this new trend, but to the younger generation it is a part of the process of bridging the gap between the way of life that they see in the towns and their own. The new urge to spend has definitely come to stay, the old emphasis on thrift is on its way out.

Two more new "arrivals" are the ubiquitous Coca-Cola stall and the butcher (generally a Christian who has moved out into the villages from Ludhiana city). Yet another new calling is that of the itinerant vegetable vendor who makes his way from house to house with a bicycle-trolley. His arrival on the scene is a sure sign that things are looking up. Fresh vegetables rarely figured on the average rural household's domestic budget in the past.

Even the interiors of many village houses now look different. A colour wash is all the rage. Bare mud walls have vanished. The *baithaks*, or the main front rooms, are liable to change from lemon yellow and shocking pink to cabbage green from one house to another. To each his own fancy!

A great deal of reconstruction has also been taking place. Villagers rarely build their houses at one go. It is invariably done in instalments, room by room. Over the last three years almost every Jat house has been converted into a brick and mortar affair. The traditional building material was a mixture of mud and *bhoosa* (straw).

The brick kilns of Ludhiana have been doing a roaring trade, and considerable damage too. The countryside is marked by huge, ugly hollows gouged out of the earth wherever a kiln has been at work.

Not surprisingly, there is also an acute shortage of carpenters who are needed not just to hack out roofing beams and make new door and window frames but also to furnish the new dwellings. The traditional *charpoys* (cots) and *moohras* (stools) are rapidly giving way to city style chairs and tables.

A taste for sofa sets, which was barely discernible three years ago, now seems to have caught on in a big way. The sofa set consists of a table, two wooden armchairs and a three-seater, woven with imitation plastic cane and upholstered with embroidered cushions, costing anything between Rs 200 and Rs 250.

The look of the courtyards too has changed. Brick paving and cemented drains are the rule. The bullock has more or less vanished and milch cattle are being moved out to new sheds and tethering posts located on *shamlat,* or village common sites. The stench of dung and urine has gone. In villages like Narangwal, where not a single buffalo is permitted within domestic compounds, there is not a fly in sight.

That all-too-familiar rural scene—a line of women fetching water from the well—is also becoming rare. The water table in Ludhiana is not far below the surface and almost every house, including that of the average Harijan, now has its own handpump.

This has brought a great deal of new business to the village blacksmith. Many of the old tongs-and-bellow establishments have grown into neat new hardware stores, retailing steel handles and G.I. and alkathene pipes plus the usual range of farm implements.

In Jodhan, the smithy has been replaced by a modern workshop equipped with a power lathe, a welding unit, an electric drill and a nozzle-grinder, all set to undertake the overhauling of a tractor from start to finish. And locals are quick to point out that Jodhan's *mistries* (mechanics) can do sophisticated work too.

Next to the private medical practitioner's clinic on the main street is a new, two month old shop which undertakes the repair of transistor radios and timepieces. This new concern is run by two brothers aged 22 and 24, both of whom were working as farm labourers till last year. Quite apart from its entertainment value, the transistor radio is rapidly emerging as a vital functional tool. Rural broadcasts provide farmers with a cheap, easy, and swift means of keeping abreast of the latest in terms of weather forecasts and market prices. And the setting up of the Punjab Agricultural University's own transmitter will soon provide farmers with access to expert advice at each crucial period of the agricultural cycle.

The significance of all this lies in the fact that it has combined to open up a new future for hundreds of masons, brick-makers, weavers, potters, tailors, leather-workers, utensil-makers, blacksmiths, carpenters, dhobis, ginners, oil-pressers, dyers, butchers, retailers, suppliers, transporters and countless others.

Despite the advancing mechanization of the farms there is an actue overall shortage of labour. Intensive cultivation means more work and wages have shot up by 200 per cent since 1961. The current busy season rate is often as much as eight rupees per day, and regulars are paid Rs 1,200 a year, plus food, clothing, two pairs of shoes and a house, compared with Rs 500 a decade ago.

There is a tractor for every 50 acres and the entire wheat crop is now handled by power-driven threshers. But even these are proving inadequate. The Ludhiana farmer is willing to spend weeks waiting in a queue outside the offices of the Agro-Industries Corporation to get his name onto the list of the favoured few whose fields are harvested by the new state-owned combines which can reap, thresh and bag the grain all in one operation, at a cost of Rs 100 per acre.

The once abundant supply of landless Harijan labourers has dried up. The more prosperous villages now compete with each other to attract *bajigars* and various other itinerant communities. Several new settlements have sprung up. Some of these are surprisingly clean, with freshly plastered mud walls in place of the old patchwork tents which used to be surrounded by a litter of dogs, scraggy chickens, donkeys and unhitched wagons.

Except in the harvest season, when wages are high, able-bodied young workers are hard to come across. Many of them have left for the mills in the city. Others are training to become tractor and tube-well mechanics. Those who are too old to learn new trades have emerged as transporters and earn between two and 12 rupees a day with streamlined mule drawn buggies that run on pneumatic tyres and old truck axles.

The creaking bullock-cart is becoming obsolete. It can no longer cope with the heavier loads that have to be carried to and from the *mandis* (markets) and the fertilizer depots. The buggies move faster and, besides, there are very few bullocks left.

There is more to the transport revolution than just this. With the rapid development of village link roads to facilitate the movement of farm supplies and surpluses the motor-car too has begun to invade village squares. The use of taxis to transport marriage parties is rapidly becoming a status symbol. Heavily overloaded Ambassador cars with their cargo of garlands, grooms *et al.* are not uncommon in June, the month of marriages.

Social attitudes too are slowly changing. There is a new emphasis on the education of women even beyond the secondary school stage. Four years ago the College of Home Science at the Punjab Agricultural University found it difficult to fill its vacancies. It is now thronged with more than four times as many applicants from farm families as it can cope with—and not all of them are the daughters of Sarpanches. Now that they can afford to live better, farmers want educated wives to look after their homes and families.

Another happy change is that more money is now spent on social centres such as the *chaupal* and the adjoining *hawa-ghar.* It is here that the greybeards of the village usually get together to listen to the news, read papers, exchange gossip and while away the time. One measure of the health of any society is the way it looks after its old people. From the contented glow that one sees on their faces in Ludhiana's villages these days it can only be concluded that all is well.

There are many who think that Ludhiana is an isolated island of progress. But this is not really true. It is the pace-setter. The story of Ludhiana is being repeated in other districts all over Punjab and Haryana. Some of the districts are not quite as successful but they are catching up. And what is happening in these two states must sooner or later make itself felt in irrigated areas all over the country.

Bibliography

Archer, W.G. : *Paintings of the Sikhs*, London, H.M.S.O., 1966.

Athwal, D. S. and Minhas, A. S. : "Wheat cultivation in Punjab", Ludhiana, Punjab Agricultural University (n.d.), *Farm Management Bulletin, No. 4.*

Ball, H. S. and Kahlon, A. S. : "Optimum resource use pattern of some mechanized farm situations in Ludhiana district", *J. Res PAU*, 4, 1967, pp. 597-602.

Billings, Martin H. and Arjan Singh.: *Farm mechanisation and the Green Revolution, 1968-84, the Punjab Case*, New Delhi, USAID, 1970.

Borlaug, N. E.: "Indian Revolution in Wheat Production", *Proceedings of the Third International Genetics Symposium*, Canberra, 1968.

Borlaug, N. E.: "Wheat, rust and people", *Phytopathology, 55*, pp 1088-1098), 1965.

Buckley, Robert Burton: *The irrigation works of India*, London, E. & F. M. Spon, 1957.

Chambers, J. D. and Mingay, G. E.: *The Agricultural Revolution, 1750-1880*, 1966.

Darling, Sir Malcolm: *Punjab peasant in debt and prosperity*, Oxford, 1947.

Duggal, S. L.: *Agricultural atlas of Punjab*, Ludhiana, Punjab Agricultural University, 1966.

F. A. O.: *Fertilizers: an annual review of World production, consumption and trade*, 1965, Rome, 1966.

Franklin, Thomas B.: *History of agriculture*, London, Bell, 1948.

Gras, Norman Scott Brian: *History of agriculture in Europe and America*, ed. by Sylvanus Urban, New York, 1925.

Hopfen, H. J.: *Farm implements for arid and tropical regions*, 2nd ed. Rome, FAO, 1971.

India: Planning Commission, Programme Evaluation Organization, *Evaluation of consolidation of holdings programme, case studies of Maharashtra, Punjab, Haryana and Uttar Pradesh*, New Delhi, 1970.

Indian Council of Agricultural Research: *Report on outstanding agricultural practices in Madras, Andhra Pradesh, Gujarat and Punjab,* New Delhi, 1964.

Johl, S. S.: "Changing face of Punjab agriculture", *Prog. Fmg.,* 6 (1), 1969, pp. 25-26.

Kahlon, A. S. and Gill, D. S.: "Economics of mechanising farm operations in Punjab", *J. Res. PAU,* 5, 1968, pp. 444-447.

Kohli, S. P.: *Wheat varieties in India,* New Delhi,ICAR, 1968.

Liebig, Justus: *Chemistry in its application to agriculture and physiology,* ed. by Lyon Playfair, from the manuscript of the author, Cambridge, John Owne, 1842.

Majumdar, G.P.: "The history of botany and allied sciences (Agriculture, medicine) arbori-horticulture in ancient India (c. 2000 B. C. to 100 A.D.)", *Archives Internationales d'Histoire and Sciences,* 14, 1951, pp. 100-133.

Mawi, Harpal Singh: *Roads in the rural Punjab,* Ludhiana, Punjab Agricultural University, 1970.

Marshall, T. H.: "Jethro Tull and the new husbandry", *Econ. Hist., Rev.* 1929-30.

Nair, Kusum: *Blossoms in the Dust; the human element in Indian development,* London, Gerald Duckworth, 1961.

National Council of Applied Economic Research: *Cropping pattern in Punjab,* New Delhi, 1966.

Owen, Wilfred: *Strategy for mobility,* Washington, 1964.

Pal, B. P.: "Towards a Green Revolution", *Times of India,* 25 March 1971.

Pathak, B. S.: "Agricultural engineering in service of the farmer", *Prog. Fmg.,* 5 (1), 1961, pp. 18-20.

Pathak, B. S.: *Some Problems of mechanisation of agriculture in Punjab,* Ludhiana, Punjab Agricultural University, 1970.

Punjab, Economic and Statistical Organization: *Punjab agriculture: facts and figures,* Chandigarh, Economic & Statistical Advisor to Govt., Punjab, 1957.

Punjab, Economic and Statistical Organization: *Statistical abstracts of Punjab,* 1967, Chandigarh, Economic and Statistical Advisor, 1968.

Randhawa, M. S.: *Farmers of India,* Vol. I, New Delhi, ICAR, 1959.

Randhawa, M. S.: *National extension service and community projects in Punjab,* Chandigarh, Community Projects Administration, 1955.

Randhawa, M. S.: *Out of the ashes,* Chandigarh, Public Relations Department, Punjab, 1954.

Randhawa, M. S., and Johl, S. S.: *New agricultural taxes and the Green Revolution in India,* Ludhiana, Punjab Agricultural University, 1969.

Raychaudhuri, S. P.: *Agriculture in ancient India,* Dacca, Dacca University, 1941.

Raychaudhuri, S. P.: *Agricultural practices in ancient India,* New Delhi, ICAR, 1953.

Saur, Carl O.: *Agricultural origins and dispersals*, New York, American Geographical Society, 1952.

Schultz, T. W.: *Transforming Traditional Agriculture*, Chicago, 1963.

Sehgal, S. R. and Gulati, A. D.: "Increase in ground water potential due to the rise of water level in canal irrigation tracts of Punjab and Haryana", *Indian Engg. J.*, 101 (49), Sept. 1968.

Trevelyan, G. M.: *Illustrated English social history*, London 4v.

Trevelyan, G. M.: *English social history: a survey of six centuries: Chaucer to Queen Victoria*, Bombay, Orient Longmans, 1968.

Uppal, H. L.: *Irrigation in Punjab*, Ludhiana, Punjab Agricultural University, 1971.

Uppal, H. L.: *Soil and ground-water survey of Punjab*, Amritsar, Land Reclamation, Irrigation and Power Research Institute, Punjab, 1964.

Ward, G. T.: *Energy as a major factor in man's development*, Montreal, McGraw Hill Univ., Brace Research Institute, 1964.

Index

Acts, *Consolidation of Holdings and Fragmentations* (1948), 40; *Cooperative Credit Societies* (1940), 81; *East Punjab Utilization of Land* (1949), 46; *Enclosures Act of England,* 43; *Patiala and East Punjab States Union Abolition of Biswedari Ordinance,* 47; *PEPSU Tenancy and Agricultural Lands* (1955), 47; *Punjab Abolitions of Ala-Malkiyat and Talukdari Rights,* 47; *Punjab Occupancy Tenants* (1952), 46; *Punjab Security of Land Tenures* (1953), 47

Agency for International Development, 66

Agency system, abolition of, 89

Agrarian economy, structure of, 45, 46

Agricultural development, services to support, 55

Agricultural machinery, depreciation of, 181

Agricultural produce, marketing of, 96, 97; processing of, 97, 98

Agricultural production, 142-144; increase in, 179

Agricultural Refinance Corporation, 89, 96

Agricultural surpluses (marketed surpluses), mobilization of, 48

Agricultural strategy, 99, 104, 181

Agriculture, educated people, productive role of, 179; human element, role of, 34-37, 178; mechanization of, 31, 140-144, 169, 194; modernization of, 32; stagnation of, 180; government's policy of giving remunerative prices for, 180, 181; requirements of, 181,182

Agriculturists, and the urban middle classes, war between, 50; *see also* Farmers

Agro-Industries, development of, 99, 100; reorganization of, 100-103; design and testing centre of, 150-152; manufacture of, 152; quality control of, 101; in the private sector, 104; role in the regeneration of (by Sikhs), 35; specialization of, 101; technical guidance of, 101, 102; types of, 146, 147

Agro-Industries Corporation, 55, 194; programme of, 148

Agronomy, improvement of, 68, 76, 77

All India Radio, Jullundur, functions of, 59; object of, 59; programmes of, 59, 60; working of, 59

All India Rural Credit Survey Report, 82

Animal Husbandry, 55, 59